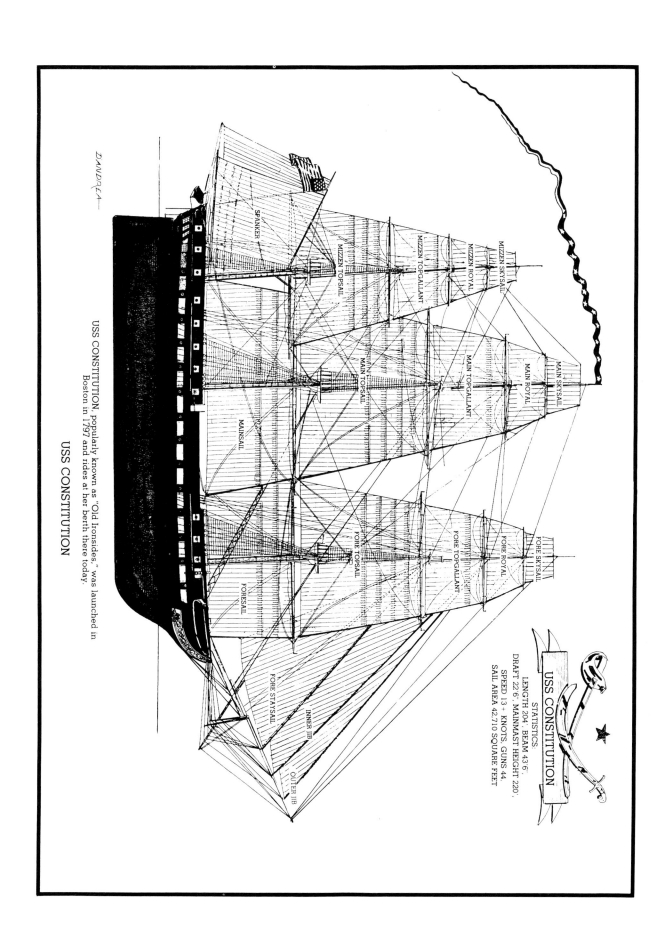

DANDREA—

USS CONSTITUTION, popularly known as "Old Ironsides," was launched in
Boston in 1797 and rides at her berth there today.

USS CONSTITUTION

SPANKER

MIZZEN TOPSAIL

MIZZEN TOPGALLANT

MIZZEN ROYAL

MIZZEN SKYSAIL

MAINSAIL

MAIN TOPSAIL

MAIN TOPGALLANT

MAIN ROYAL

MAIN SKYSAIL

FORESAIL

FORE TOPSAIL

FORE TOPGALLANT

FORE ROYAL

FORE SKYSAIL

FORE STAYSAIL

INNER JIB

OUTER JIB

USS CONSTITUTION
STATISTICS:
LENGTH 204', BEAM 43'6',
DRAFT 22'6', MAINMAST HEIGHT 220',
SPEED 13 + KNOTS, GUNS 44,
SAIL AREA 42,710 SQUARE FEET

Around the World in Old Ironsides: The Voyage of USS *Constitution*, 1844–1846

Around the World in Old Ironsides: The Voyage of USS *Constitution*, 1844–1846

To commemorate the 150th anniversary of this voyage

By Ship's Carpenter
Henry George Thomas

Edited by
Alan B. Flanders

BRANDYLANE PUBLISHERS • Lively, Virginia
in cooperation with the
Norfolk County Historical Society, Chesapeake, Virginia

Brandylane Publishers, Lively, Virginia 22507

Library of Congress Cataloging in Publication Data

Thomas, Henry George
  Around the world in Old Ironsides : the voyage of USS
  Constitution, 1844–1846 / by ship's carpenter Henry George Thomas ;
  edited by Alan B. Flanders.
      p.   cm.
  ISBN 0-9627635-5-1 (cloth) : $24.95. -- ISBN 0-9627635-6-X (pbk.)
: $19.95
  1. Constitution (Frigate) 2. Voyages around the world.
I. Flanders, Alan. B. II. Title
VA65.C7T47 1993
359.3 225--dc20   93-15295
                                             CIP

ACKNOWLEDGEMENTS

The editor of this work wishes to first thank Mrs. Ruth Kevill Richards for the generosity she extended in allowing this precious family heirloom to be published. Because of her preservation of the Thomas journal, the rest of the nation may now learn more about this most famous ship and her ancestor, ship's carpenter, Henry George Thomas. I would also like to express my sincere gratitude to the family of Ruth Kevill Richards for their cooperation in this project.

I would also like to thank the members of the Northwest Historical Society, whose board members are listed in the foreword, for their initial interest in having the Thomas journal published. It was because of their generosity that an early working draft was written and presented to the United States Naval Academy for review.

This project could not have been started or completed, however, without the sponsorship of the Norfolk County Historical Society of Chesapeake, Chesapeake, Virginia. The editor is particularly grateful to society board members Mrs. Elizabeth Hanbury and Mr. Elmer Sawyer for their steadfast support. Their contributions were key factors that made the publication of this book possible. The entire membership of the Norfolk County Historical Society is also recognized for their interest in seeing this book published.

Mrs. Kathryn Winslow of the Daughters of the American Revolution, Great Bridge Chapter, was also a major contributor towards this publication.

Dr. James Morris, historian, author and faculty member of the Christopher Newport University, is also recognized as having given time and editorial comment, written and otherwise, to this manuscript. His suggestions for defining obscure nautical terms, identifying historical place names, charting the voyage and placing a sail plan in the appendix were warmly appreciated and applied.

The library staff of the Mariner's Museum, Newport News, Virginia, provided much original material surrounding this voyage including unwritten resources mentioned in the foreword.

From the conception of this project, the spirit of the late historian Dr. Thomas T. Hamilton of Old Dominion University has been part of this project. His enthusiasm and early recognition that Thomas's story should be published have served as constant beacons for this editor to "get the Constitution around the world."

Robert H. Pruett and his staff at Brandylane Publishers, Lively, Virginia deserve high praise for their patience and steadfast dedication to excellence in their profession. Many of their adroit and timely ideas and concepts are part of the contents of this book. LCDR John Jones, USN, agreed to be the navigator for the project and drew the charts from Thomas's original citations.

And finally my family, who have made the sacrifice of allowing a husband and father to sail for a while with "Old Ironsides," deserves a thank you. Leslie Flanders, my wife who has now weathered three books with me, my eight-year-old daughter Shannon, and four-year-old son Nicholas have shown true generosity and good spirit throughout.

Dedicated to the crew of the
USS *Constitution* past, present, and future,
and to the best shipmates any writer could have:
Leslie, Shannon, and Nicholas Flanders

FOREWORD

As long as there are those interested in the lore of the sea, there will remain a constant need to hear and preserve the words of those who have matched their daring and skill against its boundless forces.

Fortunately, many earlier mariners not only knew how to sail the oceans of our earth but also had the patience and foresight to record their adventures. It is indeed a wonder that these accounts, often stored in logbooks and journals, were saved at all and passed down through the ages. It is even more remarkable that the memoirs of not only commanding officers but also of men like Norfolk's Henry George Thomas, ship's carpenter, were preserved. But his account of a voyage that began at Gosport Shipyard, adjacent to Portsmouth, Virginia, now the site of the Norfolk Naval Shipyard, in the early spring of 1844 aboard the nation's most famous ship, USS *Constitution*, "Old Ironsides," and resulted in the circumnavigation of the globe is a story of wonders and miracles. Because of Thomas's daily entries into his journal, we can now come to know this ship, her commander Captain John "Madjack" Percival, officers, crew and the events that transpired during their two and one-half years at sea. Unbelievable as it might seem, a very complete story of this, Old Ironsides's longest and most challenging voyage, has remained untold for over a century. Because of the preservation of the Thomas journal by the author's family, and the care given it by his great, great granddaughter, Mrs. Ruth Kevill Richards of Portsmouth, Virginia, it has survived in excellent condition. Through her generosity, it was made available for publication. Members of the Northwest Nautical Association, Portland, Oregon, gave initial support to have the journal edited. Because of the involvement of W.L. Robillard, Everett E. Jones, M.D., Kenneth A. Manske and Captain David Engen, a draft was sent to the United States Naval Academy History Department where it was studied with great interest. Judging that the Thomas journal is indeed a national historic treasure that should be available to the public, the Norfolk County Historical Society of Chesapeake, Virginia, with a supplemental grant from the Great Bridge Chapter of the Daughters of the American Revolution, sponsored this publication.

Around the World in Old Ironsides is more than just a logbook that notes in outline form the information that Navy officials of that day demanded. Although Thomas arranged his personal journal in the format of a logbook, with dates and exact positions by longitude and latitude above each entry, his record is far more than records of weather and redundant sea conditions. Because of his duties as ship's carpenter, Thomas kept a continuous account of USS *Constitution*'s maintenance and modification during actual operations. Thomas also took time during some 30 port calls to write highly descriptive accounts of the landfalls of the Madeira Islands, Tenerife, Rio de Janeiro, Mozambique, Zanzibar, Qullah Battoo, Touron Bay (Danang, Vietnam), Valparaiso and others. Thus the Thomas journal evolved into an unusual combination of log, ship's journal and personal travelogue. In addition to her other duties, USS *Constitution* served as a scientific laboratory for Dr. Reinhardt, the official botanist of Philadelphia who, assisted by ship's surgeon McCloud, collected and catalogued various flora found in those distant lands and also conducted early medical research on the origins of yellow fever. Fortunately Thomas copied their work and findings into his journal. The geographical differences of the worlds he saw were also patiently and often elegantly recorded by Thomas. We also learn from the Thomas journal that during the voyage, Captain Percival was ordered to experiment with various hull paint for temperature control below decks.

But why sail America's most prestigious warship around the world? In the first pages of the journal, Thomas describes the Constitution's political, diplomatic and military missions. The year 1844 was filled with challenge for the newly emerging world power of the United States. Skirmishes between American settlers in the southwestern territories and Mexico coupled with a boundary dispute between America and Canada over the Oregon territory were daily bringing the United States closer to war with both Mexico and Great Britain. Therefore almost immediately after Constitution left Gosport, the crew was exercised at their guns and briefed about the possibilities of armed conflict. Meanwhile, America's European trading competitors were busy fortifying international ports and trying to close some of them off to United States trade. Intelligence about these new fortifications was needed, and therefore liberty calls in port were used for observation and intelligence gathering. Since the United States had signed a treaty outlawing the international slave trade, the issue of smuggling had become a real problem. Therefore when Thomas and the Constitution put to sea, their mission was a complex one. Not only had they to "show the flag" at all assigned ports-of-call, but they also were ordered to observe and record all foreign military operations. They were also tasked to stop and board any suspicious ships that might be transporting slaves. The ship was further assigned to transport the United States' first ambassador, Henry A. Wise of Virginia, to Brazil, to his new official residence in South America. Official communications concerning the future war with Mexico and international friction with Spain and England are also addressed with the ship reaching the coast of California as the Mexican War broke out. Among the many other assignments, if called upon, Constitution was tasked to assist neutral nations and their citizens. One such incident during the voyage led to the direct military intervention of United States sailors and marines as they stormed ashore at Touron Bay in Cochin China, later Vietnam, to free a French bishop being held hostage. This action marked America's first land engagement in Southeast Asia! From pirate attacks to America's first military action in Southeast Asia, the Thomas journal brings to life one of the most eventful voyages on one of the most famous ships of the nineteenth century.

As the crew readies the ship in Gosport, Virginia, and sails past the Virginia capes, Thomas's narrative is alive with action. While some of the crew busily man the yardarms and set sails, others are working the gun carriages and repairing the rigging. Thomas takes the reader from the lookouts into the holds and from bow to stern with vivid pictures of a great sailing warship underway. Thomas's entries are left as much as possible in the original style of their author. Where complex or obscure nautical terms are used, simplified definitions have been provided in the text from Peter Kemp's *The Oxford Companion to Ships and Sea* and Alexander Crosby Brown's *Sea-Lingo*. Dr. James Morris, maritime historian and author from Christopher Newport University, Newport News, Virginia, also contributed valuable editorial and historical commentary. A sail plan of the Constitution to facilitate the location of sails, lines and various rigging with a synopsis of her history were added at the end of the manuscript. *Around the World in Old Ironsides* is divided into three major section titles: the Atlantic Voyage, the Indian Ocean Voyage and the South China Sea and Pacific Voyages. These sections were not used by Thomas, but have been added to serve as a division for the reader who might wish to concentrate on a particular part of the cruise. However, the actual sequence of entries as written by Thomas is strictly followed, thus allowing the reader to plot the course of the Constitution from 1844 through 1846.

In addition to the Thomas journal, the memoir of Ship's Clerk Benjamin Franklin Stevens and the letterbook of Midshipman Lucius M. Mason are also interwoven throughout the manuscript. Both sources are available in the Mariners' Museum Library, Newport News, Virginia, and were used to add further dimension to Thomas's observations. The Stevens memoir, published years after the voyage, contains some colorful details about various port calls. Tragically, Midshipman Mason died at sea, but his letters contain some youthful perspectives of incidents during liberty ashore and while underway, particularly while sailing around the Cape of Good Hope.

However, Ship's Carpenter Henry George Thomas is the principal narrator for this story and his journal stands alone as the most complete record of the Constitution's around-the-world voyage yet discovered. Therefore, the journal you are about to examine reads exactly the way Henry George Thomas intended, as if he had handed it to you personally when he returned home to Gosport, Virginia.

"Captain Percival has what most captains do not, that is he has implicit confidence in his abilities to run or manage a ship. He works a ship with the same confidence, and with no more fear of making a mistake, than a skillful musician fears making a mistake in a piece of music. My only wish is that more commanders felt the way that our Captain Percival felt towards the proper handling of a ship. To watch him is to watch a fine surgeon at work, and he takes his work as seriously as a physician as well"

Midshipman Lucius M. Mason's description of Captain John "Madjack" Percival during USS Constitution's voyage around the world.

Table of Contents

Actual navigational charts produced from George Thomas's journals of USS *Constitution's* voyage are provided throughout the text.
Editor's Note: The placement of page numbers, title and chapter headings reflects the addition of these unnumbered navigational charts.

Henry George Thomas, Ship's Carpenter, USS *Constitution*
(Photo provided courtesy of Mrs. Ruth K. Richards)

Chapter One

The Atlantic Voyage

Navy Yard, Gosport, Virginia

Tuesday, March 26, 1844 -- Commences with light airs from the South and West and clear and pleasant weather.

List of Officers
Captain John Percival
Lieutenant Amasa Paine 1st.
    "   Wm. C. Chaplin 2nd.
    "   James Alden 3rd.
    "   James W. Cook 4th.
    "   John B. Dale 5th.
    "   Fabius Slanben 6th.
Surgeon McCloud, Purser Thomas M. Taylor
Acting Master G.W. Grant, 2nd. Lieutenant of Marines S.W. Curtis
Professor of Mathematics E. Eastbrook
Assistant Surgeon Marius Duvalis R. McSherry

Passed Midshipmen Robert Knopp
Midshipmen:
Colville Terreth
Lewis Beard
A.F. Warley
W.W. Davidson
John E. Hopson
Charles F. Collin
Cornelius Comegys
Wm. P. Buckner
John E. Hart
Lucius M. Mason*
[*died on the voyage]
J. J. Cook
George B. Douglas
Dominick Lynch
Captains Clerk B.F. Stevens
Boatswain R. Simpson
Gunner George Sirian
Carpenter H. G. Thomas
Sail Maker Issac Whitney
Mastermate Charles Woodland

Received a draft of men onboard from the Pennsylvania.

Gosport, Virginia

Wednesday, March 27, 1844 -- Commences with moderate breezes and pleasant weather. We got the launch and spare topmast inboard. There are many painters from the yard employed all over the ship, but especially around the hull.

We have been busy in the carpenter department getting small boats fastened with much help from the yard's carpenter. The boatswain reported taking onboard a great quantity of running rigging. With a voyage of this nature we will probably run through a great amount. We have also been stowing spars and trying to fit rigging tightly. Many of the new midshipmen have great difficulty in this area. We could see the battleship Pennsylvania across the Elizabeth River and I noticed she lowered her colours to halfmast. I asked Captain Percival if we should do the same and he immediately lowered our colours in response. I never found out the reason for the signal.

[Captain "Madjack" Percival, age 66, was one of America's most legendary naval officers. Born in 1778, he had served as a midshipman in the early days of the United States Navy and saw action in the War of 1812. He also commanded the first American expedition to Hawaii aboard the 12-gun schooner USS *Dolphin* on January 9, 1826. He was much admired by his fellow naval officers and crewmen during service and retirement.]

Saturday, March 30, 1844 -- Commences now with light variable winds and foul weather. Rain getting heavy at times. Captain Percival has just arrived and is preparing to inspect the Carpenter's Department. There is no real way for me to know if everything is in readiness yet. We still have no report from the Ship's Clerk Mr. Stevens.

I have had the yard shop prepare five new fishes [braces] to repair broken masts and yards during our coming voyage. These times seem troubled as the stories are passed about the ship and amongst the crew concerning our destination. What is definite is that we will be often running in dangerous waters. For that purpose I have rushed the work to prepare new gun carriages for our long guns as well as the carronade.

Sunday, March 31, 1844 -- We have taken on a supply of fresh provisions and fresh water is being stored in our tanks. The voyage must not be too far off as the stories and rumours abound.

Tuesday, April 2, 1844 -- We are busy loading supplies for the Burser, Gunner, Armourer and Boatswain Department including for 83 coils spun yarn, 2 coils houseline and various splicing equipment for the Boatswain. I also had 10 new water tanks built and placed in position. From the proposed length of our voyage, we will need all the extra water we can get.

Despite the crew's general dislike, we have also purchased 80 ship's scrapers for hull work, 100 hickory brooms and 66 corn brooms for deck work. Seventy-five rocket staves for signalling have also been brought onboard. One-thousand pounds of square and flat iron, 10 barrels of charcoal and 214 pounds of bar steel have been stored for cannon repair.

Tomorrow, I am suppose to receive the barrels of pitch and resin I ordered to do repairs when we are at sea. Meanwhile the Captain grumbles as he has not received his cook, James Dunnger, from the Pennsylvania as yet. At any rate we have received six boxes of Percival's favorite cigars.

Monday, April 5, 1844 -- We received this morning seven apprentice boys from the Pennsylvania. It made me feel rather sad to see those so young and tender in years and experience casting their lot with a such a varied and foreign crew. But for want of education, and if God was willing, these boys might survive and live out their lives as veteran seamen. At 10:00 a.m. all hands were called to muster.

Thursday, April 11, 1844 -- Two of my men, Robert Keys and John Hatch returned from liberty in Gosport. They were several hours late but gave their excuses as busy trying to gather articles for the Captain and officers quarters. They had the articles in hand, which were several ornate washstands and several small sofas. The watch did not report them this time as their scavenging had become an art to them and a boon to the ship.

Friday, April 12, 1844 -- The day commenced with light airs and pleasant. At 3:00 p.m. we left the moorings off the Gosport Navy Yard and stood down the Elizabeth River under jib and spanker. The U.S. *Steamer Engineer* alongside towed us. At 3:30, the steamer cast off and we let go the slash anchor in five fathoms of water just off the Naval Hospital.

Captain Percival addressed the crew with the vessel's rules and regulations. Most of the crew and especially the midshipmen held him in great reverence and not so much because of his age which was four times greater than theirs, but rather because he had become something of a tradition of the old navy days. After the swearing of allegiance and honor the crew was mustered to quarters at 11:00.

John "Mad Jack" Percival. Courtesy of Percival family descendants (Private Collection).

Wednesday, April 17, 1844 -- This was our fated day of reaching sight of the Atlantic Ocean. We had light and favorable breezes from the Northeast. We received from the tow-ship Engineer seven more seamen and the Captain's cook at last. At 1:30, we tacked the ship. At 2:20, we came to by using our starboard anchor in seven fathoms (one fathom equals six feet), then it veered to eight fathoms of water.

We sighted the Cape Henry Lighthouse (Cape Henry, Virginia Beach, Virginia) at compass Southeast by East 1/2. We then discharged our pilot and left the Bay of Lynhaven and headed into the Atlantic.

There were many of the brave and roughened seamen onboard who were not afraid to utter their prayers and oaths vocally at that moment, for no seaman, young or old, knows what fates both good and evil might await him outside the sight of land. [From this point in the manuscript, Thomas omits the day and simply gives the date before each entry].

April 18, 1844 -- With moderate breezes and pleasant weather we set the main top gallant sail and I noticed the apprentice boys at their dangerous work high in the rigging.

Around 4:00 p.m. Captain Percival invited the officers and gentlemen onboard to his stateroom for a social call. A light spirit was served that caused some to openly disapprove at this unnatural time in the day.

The Captain informed us that we would be picking up Governor Henry A. Wise of Virginia and his family in New York and that the family of the Honourable Governor would also be along as far as Rio where he would take over a diplomatic position [Governor Wise became the first U.S. Ambassador to Brazil]. Captain Percival made a point of telling us that the Governor's daughter was of marriageable age and that he felt as gentlemen it would be our duty to see to it that certain dress codes would have to be strictly enforced amongst all the crew. Later that evening there was some grumbling in the crew about "strict enforcement," but otherwise most agreed that the warning and pledge of officers to see that it was carried out was appropriate. A reward was announced that, without incidents, the crew would be allowed to choose several ports of entry later in the cruise. I later found this to be a habit with Percival.

[Apparently fellow Virginians Henry George Thomas and Governor Wise developed a friendship as a reference letter written by Wise after the voyage testifies to their mutual admiration. Describing Thomas, Wise wrote, "He is an energetic young man of spirit and intelligence highly becoming his office in the service of the United States and has the confidence of Captain Percival."]

At 6:00 p.m. the crew was mustered at quarters. We took in our topgallant sail and tacked the ship to the north and west. At 7:30, we took three reefs [drew in the sail or shortened the sail] and furled the mizzen [took in the main sail of the third, aftermost mast of a three-masted square-rigger]. We sighted a brig standing to the south but could not distinguish her pennant, but many guessed she was one of ours. About this time the weather turned rough and foul and once again my thoughts were carried to the dangers aloft in the rigging and the boys who risked life and limb to carry out the orders from the sailing master below.

Towards midnight, we found ourselves in the middle of a gale. The rain began to blow across the deck, at times it never seemed to land but rather to go clear across the ship and then over the side. With the storm blowing as loud as I ever heard, I knew few would sleep that night. It would be daybreak before we lasted the storm out. There was no real sun the next day as we were enshrouded in heavy mists and fog. Those aloft hauled in much sail and proceeded with their work very carefully. We sounded bottom often with our lead and line as our sight was now completely cut off. We found a shelly bottom at 16 fathoms.

The foul weather stayed with us as well as the fog, which was heavy at times. The air was heavy with water and after any exertion, it was difficult to get a full draught of air. Even in this condition, Captain Percival inspected the crew regularly. Despite some of the grumblings in rank while waiting for inspection, it always seemed to reinsure the hearts of many how confident the Captain and other officers appeared on such occasions. Yet there seemed no panacea for the seasickness that spread widely throughout this veteran crew. The only relief the men enjoyed was the sighting in the thick fog of a small schooner to our leeward.

Much to our surprise the schooner closed quickly and raised a pennant to inform us that she had a pilot aboard. Little did I know how far we had come that week with the storm. But the men now cheered when the pilot came aboard, for Sandy Hook, New York, was certain not to be too far off. I heard later from the pilot that he was ordered out sooner than normal as the weather had not cleared around New York.

April 25, 1844 -- To the great relief and cheer of the men, we sighted the Sandy Hook lightship as the fog finally began to lift. Our compass reading placed her as North Northwest, Sandy Hook, Northwest 1/2 West. Shortly after 2:30 p.m., we got underway and stood in towards the entrance to Sandy Hook. We could soon make out several sails standing in at 4:45. Pulled up and fastened the sails and came to with the starboard anchor in 16 fathoms.

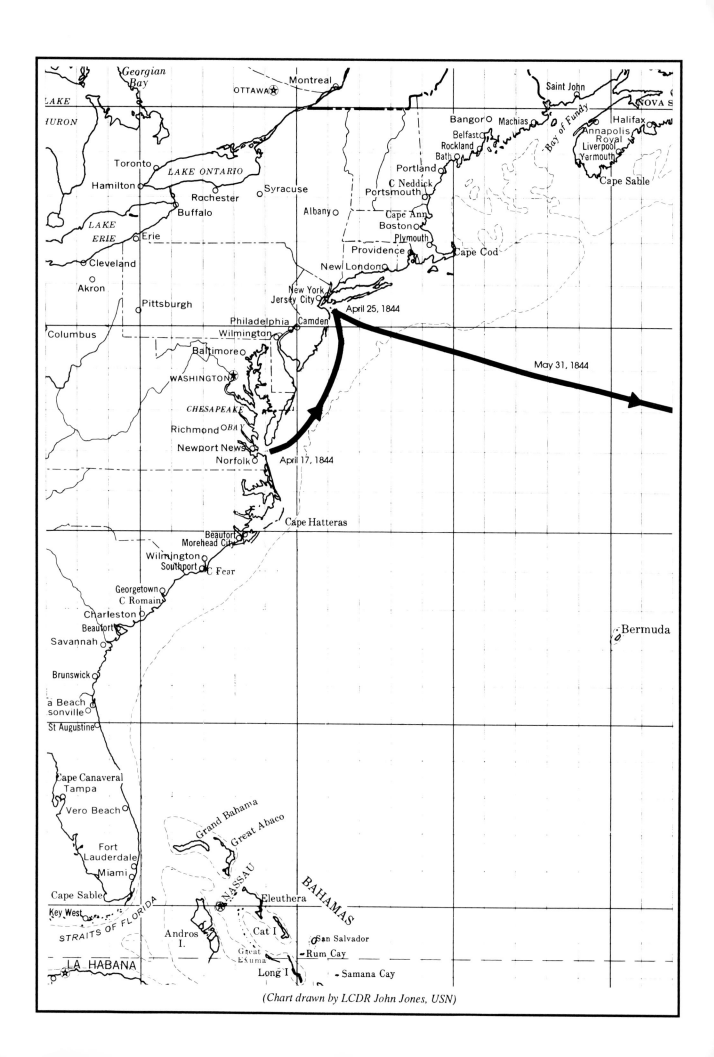

(*Chart drawn by LCDR John Jones, USN*)

The fog that had followed us up the Atlantic caught up with us again and seemed to dim the happiness that spread throughout the ship after such a journey.

April 26, 1844 -- A steamer came alongside from New York at 11:45. All hands were called out and we got underway toward the harbor with our top gallant sails. Our top sails, jib and spanker easily caught the full wind; the fog lifted once again and this time the crew prays it is for good.

New York

April 28, 1844 -- At 12:00 mid-day, we made our number [Pennants were raised for identification.] to the U.S. Ship *North Carolina* and fired a salute of 13 guns which was promptly returned from her with nine guns. At 1:30, we clewed up and came to off the Battery in eight fathoms. At 3:30, we moored the ship with four and one-half fathoms on the starboard stream anchor.

We sent a party of men on liberty. Captain Percival mentioned to me that Seaman John Swift had been shipped out for being a slippery character. We were terribly short of seamen, but the voyage suffered us little because of that. We soon, however, received 50 seamen from the North Carolina and 42 ordinary seamen. I welcomed four carpenters and two joiners onboard from the shipyard for minor repairs. [Normally the crew totalled 450 officers and men.]

Here we also took on Governor Henry A. Wise and his family. He was to become Minister to Brazil and one of our early duties was to transport him to his diplomatic post. His family seemed to take an instant liking to the vessel. The crew seemed slightly indisposed at the laughter and frivolity shown by the officers towards Mrs. Wise and [her] daughter as they had been previously warned not to offend the family.

It was widely known that the Honourable Mr. Wise was much excited about the opportunity to sail on the Constitution. Several newspapers printed his letter stating his great regard for the ship. The Captain in responding in kind gave the Wise family his room and quarters.

Captain Percival was in an excellent mood as he had a long visit with his family in New York. The two families were then received onboard and spent over four days on ship much to the pleasure of Captain Percival. Many an officer turned his head toward the good fortune of having two lovely young ladies onboard, both Percival and Wise having daughters.

We spent much time ashore as the vessel was further secured for the voyage ahead. A company consisting of Captain's Clerk B.F. Stevens, various officers, including

Gunnery Practice (Photo provided courtesy USN. Photo by Margie J. Shaw).

Captain Percival and myself, would venture into the city to frequent the theaters. There was much entertainment on our shore visits. As always, we would all miss New York after leaving her for the high seas. As the Captain had ordered a new galley to replace the old one, the officers tried frequently to dine ashore.

Young Midshipman Lucius Mason rejoined our ship today. He stated that he had arrived in New York several days earlier than we did and was now bored of the city. Such is the life of a young man who, once out to sea, will yearn for a room on land.

Most of the time on ship we have been trying to see that none of the many visitors we received will get hurt or lost. This has become somewhat of a nuisance as many ask and repeat again the same question, "Is this the same Old Constitution that won so much fame in the war?" The men have generally remained hospitable towards them and have tried to explain everything to them that is at all worth knowing.

May 25, 1844 -- We took on seven more apprentices and still more crewmen, now almost making a full crew. Received more sand as well for our fires. The harbor has been extremely busy with other ships of war. We have joined the U.S.S. North Carolina in gunnery practice. The Sloop-of-War John Adams [launched in 1830 at Gosport, Virginia] anchored nearby and Commodore Jacob Jones visited the ship. [Jones was notable for his capture of the British brig-of-war *Frolic* while in command of the sloop-of-war *Wasp* during the War of 1812.]

May 29, 1844 -- Commenced with light breezes from the north and west with pleasant weather. At 9:30, we received a pilot. We also hoisted onboard two very well made cutters [a small auxiliary, usually 24-32 feet long with eight to fourteen oars and sail]. I was particularly proud of them since I had directed their construction. At 11:30, we got underway in tow of the Steamer Hercules.

Standing Out

Thursday, May 30, 1844 -- Commenced with light breezes and pleasant weather. The U.S. Ship of the Line Columbus manned her rigging and gave us three cheers which was returned by our crew. At 7:30, we cast off the Hercules and made sail to royals and flying jib. Took our departure at 8:00 p.m. Sandy Hook Lighthouse bearing for compass North Northwest at a distance of eight miles. Got the anchors on the bows and secured them for sea. The crew was inspected at quarters. We passed an English barque and showed her our colours. Latitude 40 degrees North/Longitude 72.55 degrees West. Distance made 58.2 miles.

[From this point in the journal, Thomas closes most of his entries with the number of miles sailed during a given 24-hour period and the ship's location by latitude and longitude.]

At Sea

May 31, 1844 -- The Constitution rode beautifully in calm seas under full sail. Many of the crew were allowed idle time onboard away from stations which doesn't come often, but was a very human act often done by Captain Percival to give the men a chance to air their quarters. Percival had mentioned to me that the Atlantic is often not predictable, especially in the Spring and that each man should have a time to air.

He was certainly right because as we made 173 miles around Latitude 39 degrees North and Longitude 68 degrees West we began to pick up rough weather. Once again the fog we rode in to New York enshrouded our vessel. Even then the Captain seemed in a particularly light mood this morning and joked openly about Clerk Steven's inability to cope with the movement of sea and ship. He said that Stevens had remarked that he missed the days of action on the high seas when every other vessel might be an enemy ship.

June 2, 1844 -- Commences with light breezes and pleasant weather. At 3:00 p.m. we braced up (adjusted a yard so that it lies closer to the fore and aft line of the ship) and took in the lower studding sail. At sunset, the Captain inspected the crew at quarters. From 8 to midnight, we had warm light breezes across our bow as we headed to the South. It was quite comfortable on deck and the sounds the ship made under sail were distinct and individual to this vessel. The quiet of the ship at this time of night is a joy to a man's heart because if he is a true lover of the sea, this is the time when the sound, the scent and quiet blend so well together as if trying to remind one of why he set out to sea in the first place.

From 8:00 a.m. to Meridian, we had light breezes and clear, pleasant weather. At 10:00 a.m., the crew was inspected at quarters. That morning at 10:30, we had divine services with Captain Percival reading from his family Bible. Then, to my great surprise and I am sure to the officers and crew, Captain Percival ordered all hands to be mustered and read the Articles of War.

There had been rumored across the entire country over the last two years of a possible war over the boundary for the Oregon Territory. There had also been talk of conflict with the Mexican State over the Texas Territory. Captain Percival wanted every man prepared in the event of news that we were at war and what particular chores and duties he might be called upon to undertake.   Percival had the Marines practiced in boarding parties and the gunners were kept busy most of the day in target practice with one of my old cutters being used for that service. We also varied course according to "textbook" situations to produce the sobering environment of an actual battle in progress. Sailors who made light of the situation were warned that such behavior in even a mock drill would be matched with severe punishment.

The family of Governor Wise seemed much amused at the drill and all affairs that day seemed to please the Captain. Percival was popular as the skipper of most vessels he had been attached to, but the Articles of War were also a warning to every man on the ship that there was an adequate and swift punishment to balance every transgression.

June 13, 1844 -- We showed our colours to what I thought to be a British barque standing to the north and west. At 2:30 p.m., we made land on the lee bow [that side of the vessel sheltered from the wind]. At 5:00 p.m., we discovered the islands to be those of Corvo and Flores [smaller islands in the Azores].   At 3:00 p.m., we took in the studdingsails, braced up at 5:00 a.m., and wore [putting a vessel on the tack by putting its stern into the wind] on the larboard [port or left side of the ship]. At 8:00 a.m., we took the following bearing, the South point of Flores bore on compass Southeast by East. The West point of Corvo took the bearing Northeast by East. Around 9:00 the studding sails were taken in. The crew was exercised at quarters. Distance made 47 miles. Latitude 39.14 north/Longitude 34.41 west.

The islands of Corvo and Flores are evidently of volcanic origin as they seem to be completely composed of lava. From the ship we could make out several hot springs, which could have been at first whales.

Sunday, June 16, 1844 -- Commences with moderate breezes and pleasant weather. Sent up and shipped a new main topmast crosstree. At 4:00 p.m. we could see the peak of Pico Island and the Island of Fayal in sight. The ship is under a single reef topsail, made and reduced sail as occasion required. At 7:10 p.m., the Southeast point of Pico bore compass reading East by Northeast. Distance made 53 miles. Latitude 38.22 north /Longitude 28.43 west.

Fayal Roads

Monday, June 17, 1844 -- Beating up for the anchorage off the town of Orta, Fayal Islands [Azores]. Got the anchors off the bows, bent the stream cable to the starboard anchor. At 8:30, clewed up and came to with the larboard anchor in 25 fathoms of water. The American Vice-Consul Dabney visited the ship. We hoisted the Portuguese Flag at the fore and fired a salute of 17 guns which was returned gun for gun from the town. This port visit should give us time to finish completing work in the patent air ports which should greatly improve the crew quarters' ventilation.

Some of our crew visited the American whaleships Arabella and Portland, both out of Sag Harbor. The former 23 days outbound for New Zealand.

The peak of Pico [another of the Azores] looks very majestic from the deck. It has the appearance of a sugar loaf or cone, with the top cut off. It looked so wonderful rising out of the clouds and it being the only high land near us, was visible for sixty miles off.

Tuesday, June 18, 1844 -- The next morning Fayal presented a beautiful appearance indeed. The sun reflecting upon the white roofs of the houses, caused them to sparkle like silver, and my time until breakfast was passed examining with the minutest attention the boats, houses, churches, etc., so entirely different from those back home.

At 7:00, we visited the home of Counsular Dabeny, who welcomed us, and invited the officers and gentlemen onboard to make the mansion their home while we were in port. The Wise family were also his guests for the four days we spent there. As American ships were rarely seen in these waters, we became a great curiosity. The Constitution was the first American frigate to have ever visited the island.

In the afternoon, a party of officers including myself went ashore and passed a very agreeable time. The streets were very narrow, and the houses are nearly all the same size; all are made of lava which also makes up the composition of the island. The convents and the churches are the only buildings that offer a variation in architecture.

A visit to the Consul's house will prove how rich in tropical plants the island is. The climate is very salubrious and vegetation flourishes all the year. The soil is decomposed lava and is said to be the richest in the world. The mercury is never above 80 degrees and rarely lower than 50 degrees. The population at last count is said to be some 30,000 inhabitants. Their major export seems to be various tropical fruits, but the area is especially known for its Pico Island pipes.. They state that they export over 18,000 pipes each year. The Peak of Pico was not scaled as its ascent is not usually undertaken even by the natives.

These islands belong to the Government of Portugal, and the governors and other high functionaries are sent directly from that country and manage to retain their offices as long as peace and quiet reign. There has been some rumour of trouble brewing in this paradise, but no particular incident as such to tip the hand of the government has occurred yet. Labor is very cheap and can always be obtained for as little as 16 cents per day and it seems the habit of the government to keep the poorer classes exactly where they are, and not spread the light of religion or education amongst them. A similar system to that which was called the feudal system can be found here. The rich always have their dependents hanging about, and allow them certain lands, the proceeds of which are to be paid over to the lord. The condition of the laboring class by this means is not much higher than that of the old English or Russian serf of the present day.

The women of the middle class wear a very peculiar dress, which gives them an extremely odd appearance; it is a large black cloak with a calash [veil] of velvet hanging over their faces. At first I supposed they might be nuns, but was afterwards assured they were only following the customs of the country.

A visit to the churches is well worth the trouble of ascending the steep hills. Gilt and wax candles are very abundant in the ornate surroundings.

On the evening of the 18th, a ball was given by the Consul in honor of the Constitution's arrival, and the Portuguese beauties turned out in great force. As many officers that could be spared from duty attended and the time was passed most pleasantly. The only problem seemed to be the amount of formality surrounding the presentation of the women, as the Portuguese seem very suspicious towards us concerning that matter. As a matter of fact the streets were often empty of even a single pretty face, but behind the latticed windows many a pretty face could be seen peering to catch a glimpse of the foreigners in port. The only disappointment experienced was that of having a silent partner. The ladies could not speak in English, and we could not talk in Portuguese, so it was a blind bargain after all. The ball broke up at two in the morning and all went back to the ship very much pleased.

The next afternoon we felt bound to return the compliment, so the quarterdeck was made ready for the reception of the guests. Flags of all the nations ornamented the ship and the guns were run out to give room for dancing. The party seemed to enjoy the visit to "Old Ironsides" and everyone retired happily. On the morning of the next day, June 20th, we took leave of our kind friends in Fayal, weighed anchor and stood out to sea.

June 20, 1844 -- Later we hove to [stopping a vessel by bringing her head near to the wind yet trimming sail and making no headway] and spoke to the American Brig Lycoming which was 35 days from Palermo and bound for Boston. We also discovered sickness aboard her and Captain Percival ordered our assistant surgeon to her. We also sent her some supplies and medicine stores to aid the crew. We got away another letter bag with her as well. At 2:30, we filled away and made all sail that could draw on our course. Later part of these 24 hours fresh breezes and pleasant weather. At 9:00, the Captain called for inspection at quarters and we also exercised the 5th division [U.S Marines]. Distance made 218 miles. Latitude 25.03, Longitude 23.09.

Monday, June 24, 1844 -- At daylight, we could make out the Island of Madeira [off the coast of Morocco] just ahead. Shortly after quarters we were standing along the southside of the Island.

Funchal Roads

At 2:40, we shortened the sail and came to with the larboard anchor in 22 fathoms of water with a very sandy bottom. We then furled our sails and took a compass bearing as follows: Punta De Cruz West by North, Loo Rock North by East and Brogen Head East by Southeast. We hoisted out my two new cutters and dropped a kedge ahead [light anchor used to move a ship from one berth to another]. We could see the Portuguese Flag in the fort and saluted it and the town with a 17 gun salute, which was promptly returned.

We were in need now of fresh water and resupplied with 10 tons of water from shore. We also were hailed from the H.M.S. America and assisted her and her steamer in getting her out of harbor with two of our other cutters. She said that she was next bound for Havana.

Thursday, June 27, 1844 -- Today began on a depressing note with the flogging of men, James Corbett and William Ray with one dozen lashes of the cat for public drunkenness and disorderly conduct. [The cat-o'-nine tails, made of nine lengths of cord with three knots in each, was commonly applied to the bare backs of nineteenth-century sailors.]

Friday, June 28, 1844 -- At 11:00 a.m., His Excellency Henry A. Wise visited the Portuguese Frigate Dianna and was saluted with 15 guns. The American Brig Odena arrived just after us from Bangor, Maine in 26 days of sail.

We soon received a visit from the health officer. The entrance rules of the Portuguese were very strict and if a ship came in at night without inspection she would be fired upon from Loo Castle. The next day, we went ashore with the use of native

A marine's fighting top position on the mast (Photo by Alan Flanders).

boats since the surf along the beaches were so rough. The boats were particularly well handled with an oarsman getting out behind us to push our craft to shore. The natives in front then got out, and the boat was carried onto shore. We never got wet at all.

We went upon invitation to dine with the Vice-Consul Baynim. The Wise family went to stay with him as had become their tradition upon reaching shore. Later, after visiting a famous convent, the Santa Clara, we were almost attacked by beggars who caught up with us and then formed a mob. We had to race the horses to finally get away.

One of the more beautiful sights of the island are the grape vineyards. There seemed to be millions upon millions of ripe grapes hanging ready to be picked. Our host, Mr. Baynim, was British, but even so, everyday he had his table and home open to us as we explored. We were soon out to sea again after wishing him a warm farewell.

At Sea

Monday, July 1, 1844 -- At daylight we made the Peak of Tenerife [the largest of the Canary Islands] on the starboard bow. At 9:00, the crew was inspected with the 1st. and 3rd. Divisions exercised. We next stood in for Tenerife.

Santa Cruz, Tenerife

Tuesday, July 2, 1844 -- Commences with moderate breezes and fair weather. Around 4:00 standing around the northeast of the Island of Tenerife. At 4:30, we clewed up all sail and let go the larboard anchor in 29 fathoms of water in a muddy bottom. We could make the center of town as compass bearing Northwest with most of Southern Point in sight, Southwest the Easterly Point in sight, East by North. At 6:40, we fired a salute with the Spanish Fort. At sunset, we took down the yards and many a sailor that evening looked upon the most sublime of all of that chain of islands and waited for shore leave.

The next day found many of the crew assigned to the assistance of the American Brig Bern of Maine. We also hoisted the Spanish Flag before we sent out our first party ashore. The whole city appeared to be heavily garrisoned as was the case with most Spanish ports.

We celebrated the Fourth of July in the officer's quarters and there was much frivolity all around. The shore fortress celebrated with a 21 gun salute. That night

Visitors examine the officers cabins aboard USS Constitution
(Photo by Margie J. Shaw, courtesy of USN).

we sent off rockets and blue lights and continued the celebration. The next day, a party of officers was formed to explore the island and ascend the peak. Many were still found to be suffering from the previous night.

After leaving Santa Cruz on horseback, we had to cross the island to the port of 'Ortava', and start afresh. We continued to ride until well within six or eight miles of the summit. We then dismounted and walked until nearing the top, one of the party was taken very ill and could hardly proceed, mostly on account of the air being so thin at this altitude.

Many of our party after a rest departed our more adventurous company, and we went little by little onward to the top. We learned later that few Americans, if any, had ever explored the summit. Dr. Reinhardt, who had been assigned to our vessel as naturalist, collected many soil samples that appeared to be made mostly of lava.

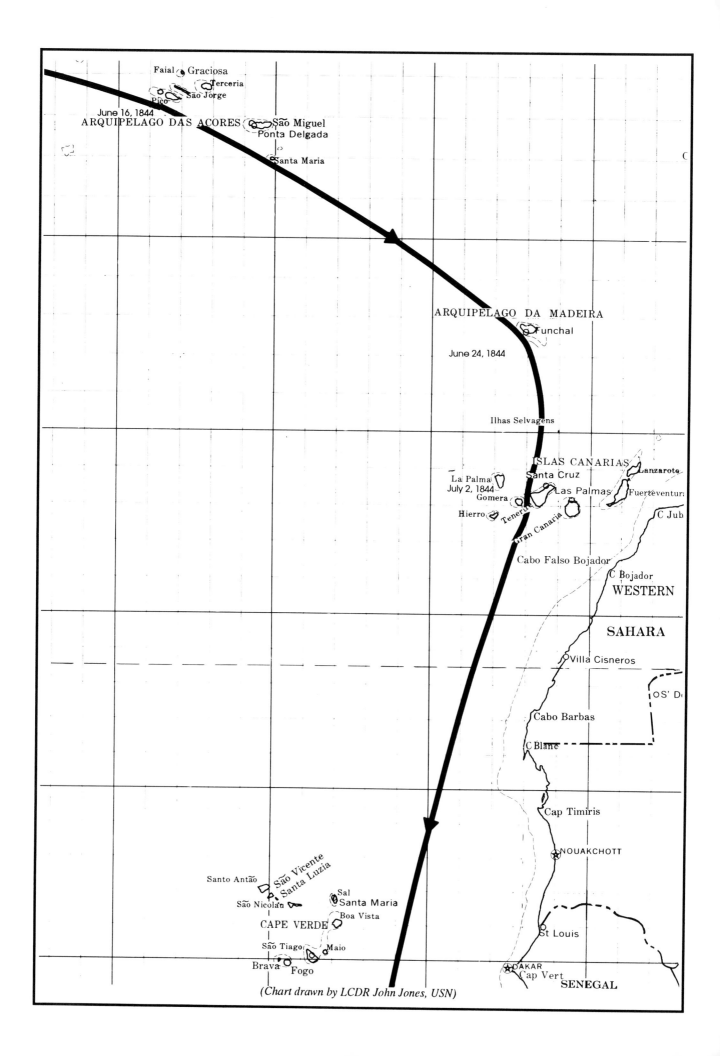

Faial ✺ Graciosa
Terceria
Pico ✺ ✺ São Jorge
June 16, 1844
ARQUIPELAGO DAS AÇORES ✺ São Miguel
Ponta Delgada
✺ Santa Maria

ARQUIPELAGO DA MADEIRA
✺ Funchal
June 24, 1844

Ilhas Selvagens

ISLAS CANARIAS
La Palma ✺ Santa Cruz
July 2, 1844 ✺ Lanzarote
Gomera ✺ Las Palmas Fuerteventura
Hierro ✺ Tenerife
Gran Canaria C Jub
Cabo Falso Bojador
C Bojador
WESTERN

SAHARA

✺ Villa Cisneros
OS' D

Cabo Barbas

C Blanc

Cap Timiris

✺ NOUAKCHOTT

São Vicente
Santo Antão ✺ Santa Luzia
São Nicolau ✺ ✺ Sal
Santa Maria
✺ Boa Vista
CAPE VERDE
São Tiago ✺ Maio
Brava ✺ Fogo
St Louis

✺ DAKAR
Cap Vert SENEGAL

(Chart drawn by LCDR John Jones, USN)

It appeared from the heat and steam just beneath the soil, say four or five inches, that the volcano on the island was still very near active. It was a terrible descent back to our ship. We were at that time as ill as those who had turned behind in the beginning. Needless to say, our ship looked good to our tired eyes but we were all sad to leave behind the wonderful Island of Tenerife.

July 5, 1844 -- We prepared to leave Tenerife and sail to Rio. [The Constitution made this crossing probably in an attempt to intercept a slave trader]. The French Corvette Berceau decided to follow along with us to our destination. She was a very friendly ship and we were able to exchange mail bags with her, as most of the men felt they were as honest and trustworthy as their own crew members. Several French officers made exchange visits with some of our officers. Early in the voyage, Captain Percival agreed to show the corvette our fire power and for a hour or so it sounded like the days of the old war. We were fortunate to have suffered little from the weather during our voyage to Rio. There was at mid-passage though a near tragedy. A young boy fell into the rigging nets and was nearly killed. The seconds in which he fell caused such a scare onboard that every seaman, young and veteran alike froze in anxiety. The surgeon was quickly attentive to him, and fortunately he was up and around in a week's time.

July 23, 1844 -- Commences with moderate breezes and pleasant weather with occasional squalls of wind and rain. During these 24 hours wind and weather pretty much the same. Made and reduced sail as the weather would permit.

At 11:30, I was standing near the mid-rail and gazing over the side. A splash in the water sounded like a dolphin or small whale. I then noticed two arms waving as we passed. I yelled to those standing near that a man was over the side and cut away the nearest life buoy.

It was a long toss and the line felt very old and dry in my hand. Had the weather been bad, we would have lost the seaman, but we were once again fortunate that day as well. When we got him back onboard I discovered it was seaman James Corbett, who had been recently punished for drunkenness. He was known as a general trouble maker and had been known to have made many enemies onboard already. Some said it was probable that he had been deliberately pushed rather than fallen by accident. The Captain ordered an inquiry into the matter but has not yet told the other officers. Captain Percival acted very quickly while Corbett was in the sea, having hoved the main topsail in a record time and lowered the cutter to retrieve him. At 12:00, we got underway again. The day ended solemnly. Distance made 168 miles. Latitude 3 degrees .14 north/Longitude 23 degrees .36 west.

Wednesday, July 24, 1844 -- "The Arrival of Neptune's Messenger." The day began with moderate breezes and pleasant weather with a few occasional squalls. Made and reduced sail as occasion required. We crossed the equator in latitude 0, and with permission from Captain Percival decided to revive an old custom of "Shaving the Green 'Uns".

At 8:00 p.m., His Oceanic Majesty's Messenger arrived with a communication from Captain Percival with his permission to commemorate the joyous occasion with a visit from Neptune himself. His Majesty arrived around 9:00 in a car attended by his train. All onboard were treated to a glass of wine or whiskey. Most of the men, I am sad to report showed a greater preference for the whiskey in unusual quantity.

Complex rigging demands knowledge and daring
(Photo by Margie J. Shaw, courtesy of USN).

Behind Neptune's car appeared six very well armed barbers to shave those who had never crossed the Dominions of His Seas. There was quite a lot of excitement as the new seamen were caught and put to the barber's pole. One of the first people to go under the treatment was the lieutenant of marines. He was led to the forecastle, placed upon a bench, and his face was well lathered with lamp tar, etc. His body was then scraped with razors, which, if they had been dignified by the name of saws, would not have taken the edge off any better.

However, before he had time to think much upon the subject, he was taken by the heels and turned topsy turvy into a tarpaulin of water, where he was received by two black bears, who washed his face and head until he called for mercy. He was at last told that he might go about his business. Thus, all who had never crossed the line were obliged to go through the ritual which varied according to the likes and dislikes of the crew. For a few of the younger men, the ritual seemed to be a bit more thorough.

Captain Percival looked on with a bemused spirit in his eye. When they got around to Governor Wise, it seemed that the Captain had already informed him as to method of bribery with a bottle of good whiskey. By 12:00, the decks were cleared and dried. All total, 150 persons had been initiated by Neptune and dunked in the royal pool--they had rigged the boom cover over the lee gangway and with the force pump filled it with water. The evening ended peacefully, even though there were scattered pranks later during the night. Distance made 149 miles. Latitude 80 degrees/Longitude 26 degrees.

July 28, 1844 -- Commences with moderate breezes and pleasant weather. We spotted a sail to our windward, but too far in the distance to identify her. At 2:30 p.m., carried away the flying jib boom, parted the larboard iron brace of the spritsail yard and sprung the dolphin striker [A jib is a triangular sail set on the stays of the foremast with larger 19th century vessels carrying as many as six jibs. A spritsail is a barren yard, no longer carrying a sail as it did previous to this period; however it was retained to because when it was braced up sharp, the spritsail yardguys opposed the pull of the jib and stays on the jibboom. A spritsail topmast, abandoned in the first half of the eighteenth century, but was retained on a yard under the jibboom until the early part of the 19th century. A dolphin striker is a short perpendicular spar under the cap of the bowsprit and used for holding down or "guying" the jibboom by means of martingales.] Furled the royals and fore topgallant sail, cleared the wreck and rigged out the boom. Set up the jib and flying jib guys, hooked a pendant tackle as a presenter martingale [also called a dolphin striker, rope or chain passing down] to the jib boom. At 6, we had an inspection of the crew at quarters. Middle part of the day was with fresh breezes and pleasant. At daylight, we pumped the ship. At 7:30, we cleeved down fore topsail and came up with the topmast rigging for the purpose of securing the top. When that was done, we set up the rigging and made sail. That morning the Captain also read us morning service from his prayer book. Distance made 188 miles. Latitude 12.05 degrees South/Longitude 32.25 degrees West.

August 1, 1844 -- Commences with light breezes and cloudy weather. A sail in sight just astern. At 5, we made a sail ahead showing the American colours. We also showed ours in return. With a pennant, she made her number which proved to be the U.S. Store Ship Erie under the command of Lieutenant Commander Duke and bound home from the Pacific.

At 5:50, we hove to. Lieutenant Commander Duke with Mr. Pendleton, former Charge d'Affaires to Chile came on board. They reported having left Rio 31 days ago. They also reported that left at Rio were the American ships U.S. Frigate Raritan, bearing the pendant of Commander D. Turner and the Frigate Congress under Captain Voorhes and the store Brig Pioneer under Lieutenant Shaw. After these gentlemen remained a short time on board, they returned to their ship. After giving us three cheers, we parted company. During the latter part of this day, the weather was pleasant. We made and reduced sail as occasion required. The Erie reported the ill health of Commodore Dallas of the Pacific Squadron. Latitude 22.35 south/ Longitude 40.31 degrees west.

Commences with moderate breezes and pleasant weather. At 5 p.m. made land ahead and the lee boom [side of the ship not exposed to the wind]. At 6:30 made the light at Cape Frio [a promontory near Rio de Janeiro, Brazil], compass bearing West. Middle part, weather pleasant. We also sighted a sail on the starboard quarter.

Got the anchors off the bows and bent the chains. Made and reduced sail as occasion required. At midnight, we made the Raza Island Light ahead [Raza Island is at the entrance of the Rio harbor]. Shortened sail and hove too with the main topsail to the mast. At 3:30, we filled away and made all drawing sail. At 8, Sugar Loaf bore compass North West by West 1/2 West, the distance was around 15 miles. At meridian standing in for Rio de Janeiro. The French Corvette Berceau in company. Distance made 110 miles. Latitude 22.58 south.

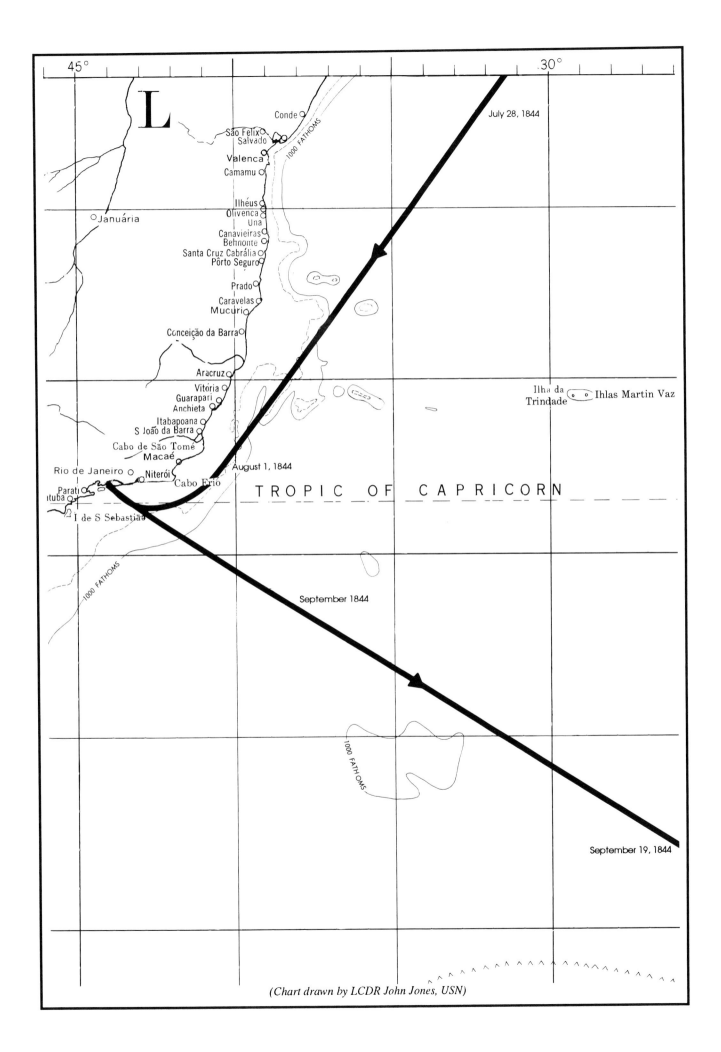

45°

30°

L

Conde

July 28, 1844

São Felix
Salvado

Valença

Camamu

Januária

Ilhéus
Olivença
Una
Canavieiras
Belmonte
Santa Cruz Cabrália
Pôrto Seguro

Prado

Caravelas
Mucuri

Conceição da Barra

Aracruz

Vitória
Guarapari
Anchieta
Itabapoana
S João da Barra
Cabo de São Tomé
Macaé

Rio de Janeiro
Niterói

August 1, 1844

Parati
ituba
I de S Sebastião

Cabo Frio

Ilha da
Trindade

Ihlas Martin Vaz

T R O P I C   O F   C A P R I C O R N

1000 FATHOMS

September 1844

1000 FATHOMS

September 19, 1844

(Chart drawn by LCDR John Jones, USN)

Harbour of Rio de Janeiro

At midnight, we hove to, the moon having become too obscure and there we waited until morning to enter the harbor of Rio de Janeiro. The Berceau had meanwhile passed us in the night and was seen becalmed [motionless because of the lack of wind] under the land.

We made out the Berceau about two miles ahead and still in calm and we soon found ourselves in the same situation. At 8 a.m. a light breeze began to make and we hove ahead of the Frenchman. But as suddenly as it had come up, the breeze deserted us and we could then see that the Berceau was shooting ahead.

We found our anchorage off the City of Rio, while she was taking in her topgallant sails. By checking the track of the Berceau later we found that she had kept more to the eastward than we had done and got the trade wind sooner than ourselves. Thus, she had sailed two or three hundred miles less than we did. Though she had beaten us in time and luck, we had beat her in distance and the French commodore agreed by giving us the Palm [the meaning is obscured by time but over the centuries a hand wave or hand signal with the open palm was a sign of peace, greeting or victory].

We next stood in for the Harbour of Rio, and exchanged numbers with the Raritan and Congress. We also saluted the pennant of Commodore Turner with 13 guns which was returned by the Flagship Raritan with her nine guns. At 3 p.m., we clewed up and came to with the larboard anchor in 13 fathoms of water. The bottom was very muddy. We then furled the sails and moored the ship with 40 fathoms on each cable. We took the following compass bearing with Island Escharles, bearing Northwest and Rat Island South by West. We then saluted the Brazilian Flag with 21 guns which was returned gun for gun.

The Honourable American Minister visited our ship. We signalled the Raritan as to the strength of other forces in the harbor, and she promptly returned our signal. We found the British Frigate Alfred and America at anchor in the harbour. We also found the French Corvette Berceau and Coquette. The "Genovese" Frigate Eurydice and a Portuguese Brig of War were nearby. The Brazilians had their own Frigate Constitution anchored. At 9 a.m., we had the crew inspected and preparations for liberty were begun.

August 4, 1844 -- Commences with light breezes and cloudy weather. Lieutenant J.P. Gillis left our ship to join the Congress and Lieutenant Gibson joined the Raritan. Also Lieutenant of Marines W.H. Lang went to the Raritan.

At 4, the ship paid its respects to the departure of Henry Wise and his family. That was a sad moment for all. The Captain publicly praised the Wise family and all agreed to join them or visit them on shore. The crew manned the yards and we saluted him with 17 guns. Ship draft forward--20 feet, 3 inches, aft--23 feet. Water made [in the hold] these 24 hours--1 inch. [At this point in the journal, Thomas began to sound the ship's hold for water because the Constitution was prone to minor leaks.]

August 5, 1844 -- It was a habit of Captain Percival to handle the minor discipline of the crew just before any visit by the crew to a port. Rio was no exception as 12 lashes of the cat-o'-nine-tails were served to George Knight, marine, Sam Harris, landsman, James Corbett, seaman, John Brown, seaman, William Mason, landsman, all for various offenses. [The term landsman refers to a crewman who has no true nautical designator, for example a helper on a survey team.]

We also sent the Congress 2,000 lbs. of powder late that evening so as not to be observed. We had the new dingy hoisted out. I was very proud of the work we had done on them. Most of the crew was not given liberty immediately as there was much scrapping to do on the ship. We did hoist several of our pennants as we heard later that the Prince of Naples was active in the harbour visiting the various national ships of war. We also learned that he had been promoted to Admiral of the Brazilian forces.

As we were not fitted out for a state visit, the Constitution remained in cover of work details. Captain Percival did not seem bothered by the fact that we were not first visited by the Prince or he kept it to himself as our work crews kept busy for several days more. Many of the men were employed in painting the outside of the ship as we would be entering tropical waters for a good part of the voyage. Our sailmakers were active in repairing sail for the Atlantic crossing and our carpenter crew was busy making a new flying jib boom. I can not forget to mention the sad news that we heard after the Frigate United States put into Rio, that Commodore Dallas of the Pacific Squadron had died.

August 17, 1844 -- The U.S. Brig Pioneer put to sea and was bound for Norfolk. We exchanged a letter bag with them as I hope that a letter might reach loved ones back home. The U.S. Ship Cyane left soon after her, and we had to help with cutters to get the Cyane out to sea. We also noticed that as soon as our ships put out to sea that the Sardinian Frigate Eurydice also was soon to follow.

CDR David M. Cashman, 62nd Commanding Officer of USS Constitution,
shows where ship's hull is seeping moisture
(Photo by Margie J. Shaw, courtesy of USN).

We received a signal from the Raritan and returned them, signal-1048. Most of the crew are now being given liberty as repairs on the ship are almost complete. Some of the men have already gotten into evil ways on shore. Joseph Yeager and Joseph Sennett were punished with 12 lashes each for insolence to Midshipman Upshur of the U.S. Frigate Congress when they were on shore leave.

August 24, 1844 -- Captain Percival informed me today that a court-martial had found guilty Midshipman R.A. Knopp and A.F. Waring; they were detached and ordered to report to the U.S. Frigate United States and returned to the United States. It should be noted that the French Sloop of War Coquette left port quite soon after the United States. We have also had a desertion from a cutter going ashore; a seaman named George Smith fled our crew and no one has reported seeing him on shore.

The Brazilians have been most helpful in returning our deserters. Recently a coloured man named Daniel Phillips deserted from the Congress and the Brazilian police had arrested him shortly after. He was of course turned over to us as the Congress has returned to sea.

August 30, 1844 -- Commences with moderate breezes from the south and the east, cloudy with light rain. Received stores on board for several departments. We sent Lieutenant Chaplin with the 1st. cutter on board the American Ship Roanoke to assist in unstepping the main mast of that ship. [Unstepping refers to the removal of the mast, a complex task since the mast and all of its rigging have to be removed.]

We sent the deserter Daniel Phillips on board the Congress after it returned to port following a short ocean cruise. The crew is variously employed, the carpenters are busily engaged at work in Eschardes Island repairing the Roanoke's main mast.

September 1, 1844 -- Captain Percival announced that Acting Master Grant was this day appointed as acting Lieutenant of this ship and also that Midshipman Strain, on leave from the Navy Department with permission to investigate the geological character of Brazil, was appointed the Acting Master. Acting Master Strain also reported for his duty.

[Ship's Clerk B.F. Stevens made the following report on Rio:

"On entering the harbor we passed the beautiful Raza Island on which a lighthouse is placed. Nothing can be conceived more delightful than this spot. It is entirely isolated and makes a very nice summer residence for gentlemen.

"Farther on we pass Fort Santa Cruz, on which a battery is placed with 300 guns. This fortification is built upon the solid rock and is supposed to be one of the strongest in the world. It presents a most warlike appearance either upon entering or leaving the harbor. All vessels are hailed from this castle, and in night are not allowed to pass it, with the exception of men-of-war.

"Nearer the city a smaller fort is seen, about halfway between Santa Cruz and the anchoring ground. It is situated upon a small island in the harbour near the shore, and commands the entire port. Ships in the daytime are all allowed to pass Fort Santa Cruz and anchor opposite the smaller battery, but if they attempt to pass the latter a shot is fired across their bow, which is followed by a ball if still persisted in, and the only satisfaction received is paying for the powder.

"The harbour of Rio de Janeiro is a regular basin or lake surrounded on all sides by the most beautiful scenery. The lake is about five miles across and from ten to twelve from the entrance to the upper part. One the right side, as we face the entrance, the city is situated, and on the left the beautiful village of Prio Grande. In the rear of the city is the high hill of Cocovado. Cocovado is seen rearing its tall summit far above the clouds. From this mountain the city is supplied with water of an excellent quality. The Organ Mountains are situated in the rear of the upper part of the shore, and all together contribute to render the harbour of Rio one of the most beautiful and is justly entitled to more praise than any place we have yet visited, and wherever one cast is eye, a landscape always meets his gaze.

"On visiting the city I was extremely gratified, and experienced much pleasure in viewing the many novelties. It being Sunday afternoon I took a walk over nearly the whole place. Stores were opened and business was transacted as usual.

"On landing the first place of interest is Palace Square. Here the Emperor's palace is situated, and fronts the harbour, and is a very neat building. The public aqueduct is also on the square, and is worthy of a visit, and a perfect bedlam is made while the slaves are drawing water. Farther on we come to the most beautiful street in the city, and the one that I had heard much while on our voyage to Rio de Janeiro.

"The Rue de Ouvidor is not entitled to any praise for the beauty of its buildings, but the variety of goods and fancy articles that are exhibited in the stores give it altogether a pleasing appearance. Here a person may purchase anything that he desires from a diamond ring to a saddle. In this street is the celebrated feather store so much spoken of, and indeed is well worth a visit. Young girls are constantly employed making flowers from feathers of various types of birds including the humming bird. Never having seen any work of this kind before, I was much pleased with observing the different forms and articles into which operatives fashioned the feathers. Only one of the girls could speak English, and she was very polite indeed to us, and we passed an hour pleasantly examining the birds and flowers.

"After leaving the Rue de Organ, the party continued on, until we reached the arches of the Cocovado, through which the city is supplied with water from the mountain. These arches cross every valley from the hill to the city, and as works of art, would do honor to many European countries. The public gardens are also well worthy of a visit. The Sunday afternoon we walked there, a band of music helped to render the time of the pedestrians as pleasant as possible. This band consisted of nearly forty member, and was pleasant as I have ever heard.

"While at anchor in the harbor, I had the opportunity of visiting the Emperor's Cathedral, though not during the service. This church is attached to the palace, so that his highness need not go out into the public to say mass, and of all places of worship I have ever seen, this was the most superb. The altar was completely covered with gilt work, while at the back and round the sides of the chapel statues of Jesus, the

Virgin Mary and the Apostles were placed. There were no galleries visible, all the worshippers kneeling upon the floor. A partition ran round the whole area, setting off about three feet of space, probably for the ladies.

"I had also the opportunity of visiting the Emperor's theater and shall long remember the event with gratification. Understanding that Dom Pedro himself will be present, we went early in order to secure good seats. The play was the Barber of Seville by the Italian company. We purchased tickets to the orchestra from persons in the streets, there being no box offices as there are back home.

"The theater is immense, and would contain two the size of the Park or Tremont [popular theaters in New York]. The whole is lighted by one great chandelier, that is hanging from the center of the dome, which is ornamented with paintings. There are fifty-four boxes on a side, contained in four rows. The Emperor's private box takes up nearly the whole of the back, and curtains were drawn before it.

"The evening being the anniversary of Dom Pedro's marriage, the house was crowded at an early hour. Those who held any rank appeared in uniform, and the sight was very imposing. I have never seen so many ladies together in a public place before.

"The Emperor did not arrive until 9 p.m. and some Englishmen who sat beside us, uttered curses very loud at being obliged to wait two hours for a boy. At last the curtains of his box were drawn and disclosed the view of the Emperor and Empress standing in front. Dom Pedro was saluted with three cheers or Vivas, to each of which he bowed his head in token I suppose of his great affection for his subjects.

"After the cheers subsided, the orchestra struck up the Brazilian National Anthem, and subsequently the curtain drew up, and displayed to view the whole operatic corps, who sang Dom Pedro's hymn, and a most beautiful piece of music it was. In the rear of the stage, the Emperor's band was stationed. The evening ended splendidly for all.

"I should also like to mention as far as possible some idea of the government, manners and customs of the people of Rio. Since the abdication of Pedro I, who is represented as being rapacious, cruel, licentious, and almost without one redeeming quality, the country has been gradually recovering from the effects of his administration, though instances can yet be cited of late rebellions in the interior of Brazil. The constitution of Brazil differs little from that of the United States, the people being represented in Congress by members chosen by themselves. The bad uses that the constitution had been put into are seen in the unsettled state of the country and the strong hold that other nations (particularly England) maintain on their rulers.

Brazil has a very great national debt, of which we are told nearly two-thirds are held by British owners, and such a thing as independence is not known in any of its commercial dealings. The slave trade has brought England in direct contact with Brazil, so much so, that the guardships of the former power are allowed to lie in the harbors of the latter. But in spite of the efforts of England, the slave trade still continues to flourish.

"Cargoes of slaves are still landed under the very guns of the British. And if by chance a vessel is taken, the slaves are out on board the guardships from thence apprenticed for the term of seven years or fourteen or even twenty years to planters. Thus England loses nothing by endeavoring to check slavery, on the contrary, rather increases its funds by this system of apprenticeship which amounts to slavery itself. The rapacity of England, otherwise called its humanity, is felt not only in Brazil, but in the Eastern world, for which seen an account of the late war with China.

"Though opposed to the above manner of emancipation, yet it is evident that his trade which has become so obnoxious to other powers will be the downfall of the prosperity of Brazil. At the lowest computation we now have learned that there are more than 1,800,000 slaves in the country entirely dependent upon their masters for support and it will be found in a few years that, as in the Southern States, the slaves cost more than they earn for their masters.

"Again the climate of Brazil engenders various cutaneous diseases in this class of its inhabitants, to which whites are often subject. I have seen blacks with their fingers and toes completely eaten off; and their feet, legs and thighs swollen as if nothing but bursting the skin could relieve them. Such are always dependent upon charity, and lie about the streets perfectly helpless. The worst degradation I have seen has been in the slaves in Brazil.

"The manners of the Brazilians are not such as to prepossess a foreigner in their favor. At the best those with whom we had dealings were but poor specimens of mankind. On the whole, I experienced from my visit to Rio de Janeiro more pleasure than I had anticipated, and was very agreeably surprised at finding my prejudices against the city unfounded. There are many curiosities in Rio and around it which time alone prevents my viewing, and which would have afforded much amusement. Before we left Rio, I received a mail package and some newspapers from home which caused me to feel richer than Queen Victoria."]

[While at Rio, Midshipman Lucius Mason experienced homesickness after meeting some former shipmates, but made some personal notes in his letterbook about the city's "fairer sex" and a ball given for the Prince and Princess of Naples:

"The morning after the arrival of the Cyane, the Brig Bainbridge arrived 45 days from New York, bringing no letters except for one or two officers from the city. On board of the Cyane, I met several of my old shipmates, whom I was glad to see, for my first cruise was on board of the Cyane.

"Shortly after that, the United States arrived--how happy I was to see her. I recollect the first time I was on board her, all the faces of my former messmates I knew perfectly but their names I could not call to mind. Visiting her was like visiting a second home. We all had such questions for each other, but often as not, when you do at last meet old friends again, the real news that can be traded is very slim indeed.

"A few days after the arrival of the United States, a ball was given on shore by the natives to which the officers of some of our ships were invited. But even after receiving such gracious invitations, many of the officers and midshipmen could not predict Captain Percival's decision as to giving his approval. A great surprise to us then occurred, as the Captain allowed us to go at 5. "We finally left the ship about 8 o'clock after trying to get a conveyance to take us out to the palace where the ball was held. We still had to trudge around another three miles before we finally arrived. However, we had the good fortune of arriving at a good time, that is after nearly everyone had arrived.

"As far as the ball, I shall not go into particulars. The Prince and Princess of Naples were both present. There is something about the face of the Prince which is very possessing, not handsome, but what one would call a decidedly good face; as for the Princess, I can not say anything in her favor, so being of the fair sex I remain silent.

"The music was good, the rooms too small, and the dancing very quick; very few of the Americans danced, the officers seemed especially shy. The dances were just too quick. The waltz was so quick as to be made faster than a spinning wheel as everyone was spun around. I refused as the other officers joined in. All in all, the evening was passed well. The Brazilian ladies were very homely, being eclipsed by some American and English ladies who were also present. There was plenty to eat and drink. The great fault was that the room was too small for the number of people collected. About midnight, being satisfied, we returned on board ship.

"After this, the Captain permitted the midshipmen to go ashore on their liberty day, that is every third day with us as we were in 3 watches; and I do not know that we enjoyed ourselves any more when we were kept on board.

"I also wish to include in this letter that our ship is painted in a lead color, with a red streak, the usual color for vessels of war. The Captain's reason for changing the color was on account of the warm climate to which we were going, a very good reason for a light color and this will not keep the body of the ship as warm as does black.

"On September 7, 1844 . . . that same day Governor Wise and his family came on board to say farewell. They had seemed like part of the crew and had made many friends of officers and seamen. There were many regrets. He said that the severance of his ties with Old Ironsides was also a final break with the United States and that at this moment he missed home too much to take the assignment. We recommended the other ships of the squadron that would make good company for him and would keep him in contact with the United States. This seemed to satisfy him a little.

"We were to go to sea the next morning at daylight and I found that I had the midnight watch, this is from midnight until 4 a.m., during which time I wrote four letters, one home to my parents and the other to a friend. I turned in to my hammock at a little after 4-and when I awoke at 7, the ship was at sea with a fine breeze off shore. So adieu to Rio and I was glad of it too for I was anxious to travel further on the voyage. Yours Truly, Lucius M. Mason."]

[Thomas Journal continues:]

September 8, 1844 -- On completion of the painting of our ship and the loading of supplies we raised anchor at sunrise and stood out to sea. At 8 we were well outside Raza Island. We were heading in the direction of the islands in the South Atlantic.

Captain Percival called all hands to witness the punishment of the crew who committed various offenses like smuggling liquor on board and drunkenness [sic] behavior. Quite a number of the nine men punished had also broken liberty and had gotten into trouble on shore.

At 9:20, Raza Island bore compass West by West, distance little more than 6 miles. We unbent the cables, secured the anchor for sea, shotted the guns. While in Rio de Janeiro, our naturalist Mr. Chandler left us and his place was supplied by Mr. Reinhardt, the famous naturalist of Philadelphia.

At Sea

September 9, 1844 -- Commences with moderate breezes and hazy weather. We discovered a sail on the weather beam. At midnight, the ship is under a single reefed topsail and single reefed foresail. At 6:00, we passed a Brig to the leeward of us about one mile. We showed English colors to her [The Constitution asked by pennant if she was of English registry.] She ran up her Swedish pennant [answering back that she was Swedish]. We have now made seven inches of water in 24 hours. Distance made 133 miles. Latitude 25.56 south/Longitude 38.52 west.

Friday, September 13, 1844 -- Commences with breezes and pleasant weather. The ship is under plain sail and by the wind we are on the larboard tack. At 8 a.m., we pumped the ship. At 9 a.m. we exercised the 4th. and 5th. divisions at quarters and the 2nd. division small armsmen. At 4 a.m. this morning the ship's deck was lighted by the fall of a very large meteor. The light resembled very much the "Blue Lights" [signal flares].

For the first time since leaving Rio, we also saw birds, though not in any quantity. They were cape pigeons, and resemble the wild pigeons in shape but not in colour. They frequently follow the ships two thousand miles, leaving them in the longitude of the Cape.

Stevens reported seeing an albatross. This bird is about the size of a swan and from wing to wing sometimes measures fifteen feet. The sailors baited a hook with a piece of fat pork, and as the ship was nearly becalmed, quite a number flocked around it. In a few minutes one was caught, and safely landed on deck. For a little while the gluttonous bird was quite seasick and vainly endeavored to lift himself from the deck, but without avail. Its eyes were large and black, and well did the poet Coleridge choose this beautiful bird for the subject of his poem of the "Ancient Mariner."

The sailors had little faith in the opinion of showing mercy to either albatross or shark. Some men onboard captured a shark soon after. Its length was around six feet and was a very fine specimen of the genus. He was caught over the stern, hauled in on the quarterdeck, carried forward by the sailors, who showed little sorrow to that seaworthy race.

September 19, 1844 -- Commences with and throughout these 24 hours light airs and calms. At 5:50, we inspected the crew at quarters. At 9 a.m., beat to quarters and the crew was exercised at firing at a target. Several pretty shots were made. At

11, beat the retreat, after expending 84 cartridges, 84 round shot, and 168 wads. Distance made seven miles. Latitude 32.54 south/Longitude 25.35 west.

[Midshipmen Lucius Mason described the target practice for the same date in his letterbook:

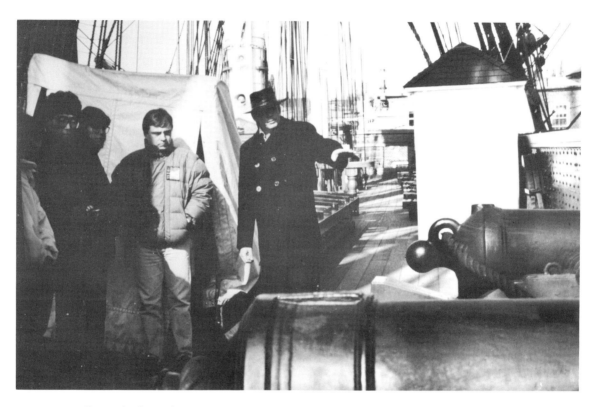

Spar deck and guns (Photo by Margie J. Shaw, courtesy of USN).

"The whole of the 19th. was perfectly calm. We employed the time firing at a target. During the exercise, we fired 3 broadsides. The target was an empty cask. There were only 2 or 3 good shots. After the exercise the cask was again brought on board."]

Tristan d'Acunha
September 23, 1844 -- On the afternoon of the 23rd., the Isle of Tristan d'Acunha [Tristan Da Cunha is located, Lat. 37.9 S., long. 15.30 W., in the south Atlantic and is approximately 15 miles in circumference] was in sight, and again we saw the English Bark and boarded her. She proved to be the Lord Eldon, from London to Bombay, and made the island for the purpose of rectifying her observations.

It had been the intention of Captain Percival to send a boat ashore, and orders were given to lie to when within five miles of the beach, but unfortunately a heavy breeze sprang up in the night, and we drifted to within two miles of it.

We then wore ship [came about], and the morning of the 24th. ushered in a gale which lasted until the night of the 25th. We were thus obliged to keep clear of the island, and stood on our way to the east. During the heaviest of the gale the ship was hove to with her main topsail to the mast, and much of the time had on her only trysails.

Her spar deck ports were frequently under water, and life lines were run around the sides. Both of her decks were wet, particularly the main, and I began to see the inconvenience and danger of a sailor's life. The frigate worked well though, and during this blow was easier and more comfortable than many other ships would have been. An account of the above island may not be uninteresting, as few are acquainted with either its locality, inhabitants or usefulness.

The group of islands situated in the South Atlantic Ocean consists of three, viz.: Inaccessible, Nightingale, and Tristan d'Acunha.

The latter island, the largest and most fertile of the group, takes its name from the celebrated Portuguese navigator. They are not often visited by merchantmen, only occasionally a whaler stops to procure refreshment. The highest land of Tristan d'Acunha can be observed sixty miles at sea and is between 7,000 and 8,000 feet in height.

All accounts of the fertility of Tristan d'Acunha are vague, though it is generally supposed to be capable of great cultivation. Its origin is volcanic, and would undoubtedly be taken advantage of, but that the harbors are extremely difficult of access. Potatoes and vegetables are raised in great abundance, and wild hogs and goats are plenty.

The other two islands of the group are entirely barren, and are always avoided by navigators. Inaccessible is about nine and Nightingale Island about seven miles in circuit. Tristan d'Acunha is about twenty-five miles in circuit, and its highest peak is 8,326 feet above the level of the sea. In the year 1811, three Americans remained on the island to prepare seal skins and oil, but left before 1813. Afterwards, a naval station was formed by the English when Bonaparte was taken to St. Helena; this was afterwards discontinued, and transferred to the Island of Ascension, where it is now. The next account of the island is up to 1821, when the ship Blenden Hall, from London for Bombay, was wrecked on Inaccessible Island on the 23rd. of June. Here the crew and passengers remained nearly six months, living on penguins and eggs [only food], until they arrived at Tristan d'Acunha in a boat made from the wreck.

On the Isle of Tristan d'Acunha, they found a Scotsman with a small colony of about twelve persons. This Scotsman was the head man on the island and was called Governor Glass. Shortly after the wreck happened, the English Sloop of War Gloucester touched at the island to make observations. A passenger, August Earle, obtained permission to visit the shore; but stopping too long, the ship was forced to put to sea, and left him on the island. Here he found the colony in a flourishing condition, one or two children having been born since the departure of the English brig. He remained on the island nearly a year, and describes it as being a most delightful spot, where vegetables of many kinds, hogs and goats were found in great abundance. His story is an interesting one, and excited great attention when it appeared. In the month of November, 1824, or 1825, he was taken off by a vessel bound to Van Damien's land.

In 1829 a vessel stopped there and reported the colony to have increased, and were very healthy; the children uncommonly so, and free from infantile diseases that are so common in the more populated countries.

The old Governor has undoubtedly been the means of saving many of his fellow creatures from a watery grave, or at least starvation on the neighboring barren islands.

This circumstance, together with a desire to see if any person or seaman or others were still on the island, induced our Captain to lie to; but in the gale, we were forced to keep away. If we had visited, interesting information might have certainly been obtained. I congratulated myself upon seeing the strange character who has passed more than thirty years of his life almost exiled from the world.

October 2, 1844 -- Commences with light breezes and cloudy weather. At 4 p.m., we spoke to the American Whale Ship "Sally Ann" of New Bedford. She was 85 days from port and bound for the North Pacific Ocean. At 4:15, we tacked the ship. At 5:15, the crew was inspected at quarters. At 6:10, we braced aback the mizzen topsails to wait for the Sally Ann. At 7, we spoke to her again and offered any assistance she might require. None being wanted, we filled away. Made and reduced sails as occasion required. Longitude-12.27 East.

October 4, 1844 -- Commences with moderate breezes and cloudy weather. Charles Crohon (OS) [ordinary seaman] was punished with eight lashes for theft. The ship is under a double-reefed topsail. At 12:15, a heavy squall from the North and West struck the ship. It carried away the cross jack yard in both quarters and split the weather clew of the main topsail. We got the wreck down and clewed up the topsail. The ship is going 9 knots under foresail. We repaired the topsail, furled the mizzen and close reefed the fore and main topsails. We made and reduced sail as the weather would permit. Ends with strong breezes and squally weather. Water made in the hold these 24 hours 13 1/2 inches. Distance made 207 miles. Latitude 36.31 South/Longitude 20.17 East.

At Sea

Cape of Good Hope

Commences with strong breezes and a heavy sea. At 3:00 p.m., we set the fore and main topgallant sails, and lee clew of the mainsail. At 2, we kept away two points. Between 2 and 3 p.m., the water became very much discoloured and the temperature indicated soundings, and according to our reckonings, we are on the Southern edge of "Cape Legullars Banks."

We heard the cry of "breakers ahead" from the topsail yard, but it proved to be nothing more than the reflection of a cloud upon the water. Near the longitude we were in, discolored water has from time to time been seen by different vessels, and in consequence of the French Brig Telemaque being the first to have discovered it, the spot off the pitch of the Cape is called Telemaque Shoals. The circumstance happened in the year 1786, and the Captain and passengers were of opinion that they had passed over a Coral bank of considerable extent, having apparently not more than two fathoms on some part of it. The danger was supposedly so imminent that they did not sound, but kept away. This spot they made in latitude 38.50 south, longitude--east from London.

Since this date several vessels have seen discolored water near the spot mentioned above, and to all appearances it extended as far as the eye could see. In 1796, 1807, and 1816, one English and two American ships saw the same appearance, and soundings of 90 to 40 fathoms were said to have been taken.

It is satisfactory to navigators to know that the supposed danger of the Telemaque Shoal no longer exists; for although said to have been seen by the above ships, yet H.M.S. Heron surveyed the spot carefully and published an account of it.

The sea at time presents curious appearances for these latitudes; as in the case of the Constitution. The clouds, for instance, will reflect the rays of the sun at certain angles and cause an appearance of breakers; again, the great quantity of animalcule

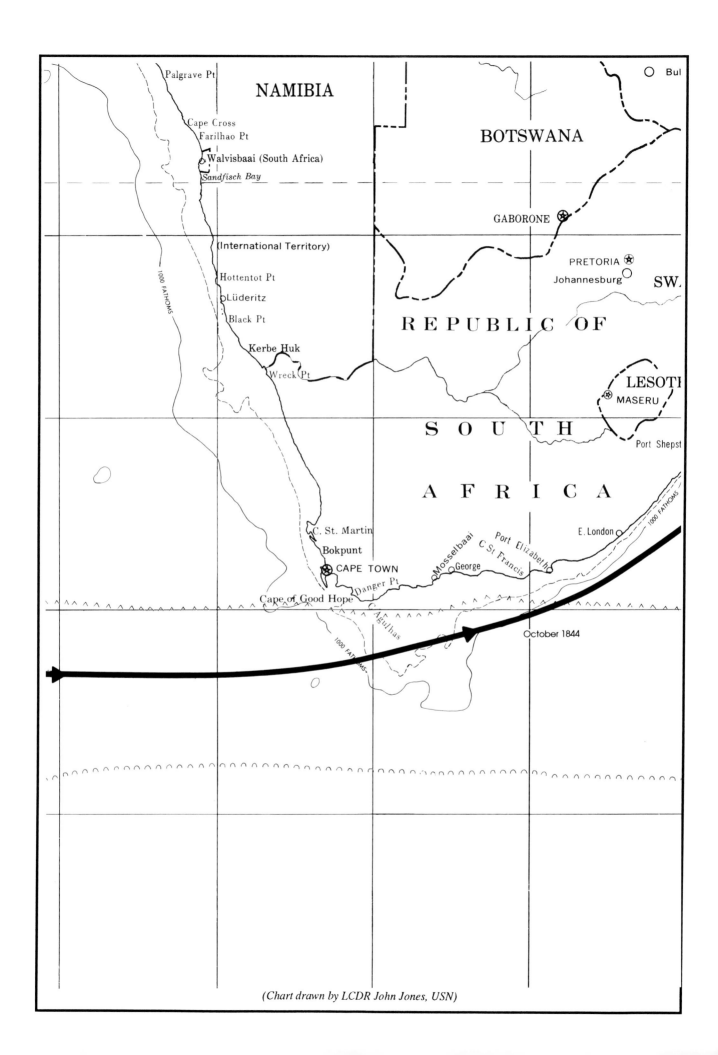

(Chart drawn by LCDR John Jones, USN)

abounding in certain seas may have caused the alarm, and vessels have been known to pass over dead bodies of whales, and this would magnify the extent. Probably the Telemaque Shoal is one of the above origins, for the fact of its non-existence is settled in the minds of navigators.

[Midshipman Lucius Mason's harrowing account of the Constitution's passage around the Cape of Good Hope follows:]

" . . . I heard on the deck that Captain Percival could see the surf breaking and that we were standing about two miles from land. The order was then given to ware ship and stand off shore, which was done.

"The sail was reduced to topsails soon after waring. We hove to with the main topsail to the mast thus lying off the Island. The wind began now to freshen into a gale, with frequent squalls of rain and hail. We were soon obliged to take 3 reefs in the fore and mizzen topsails and two in the main topsails. The courses in the topsail were also furled. I was sent up into the fore top to attend to reefing the fore topsail. It was cold and rainy. Squalls of hail would pass over us every five or six minutes.

"As I climbed up the rigging and looked out on the heavy sea as it rolled towards us, with the cold wind, rain and hail beating down upon us; I thought of the sentiment, happiness and pleasure of going to sea, of being on the boundless ocean, that element, which is so often made the subject of the beautiful song or poetry. But never was a more erroneous idea entertained, for no life can a man lead wherein he sees more hardship, and deprivation, and at the same time reaps less reputation.

"After about a half-hour, occupied by my looking over the top, thinking of persons and scenes far away, the sail was reefed, hoisted and promptly trimmed. I finally came down on the deck again.

"A short time after I had left the deck, the gale and sea increased. All the topsails were furled and we laid under dry sails.

" . . . The most water we made in twenty-four hours was seventeen inches. The ship does not leak so much in the hold as she seems to leak above water, I mean in the seams of her sides. Scarcely any bunks belonging to the officers are fit to sleep in on account of the leaking through the ways. The bunks are placed up against the side of the ship. I noted the gale was not long enough duration to prove what she would do, to tell the fact, I think she did better than I expected.

"But as far as my judgement goes, I think she is far from being in a fit condition to weather a truly heavy gale of fifteen to twenty days, which is frequently seen off this Cape of Good Hope. I do not believe she would stand another strong gale as we had the other day. This gale also loosened badly the oakum that was applied back in Norfolk last winter; so that being in a gale now would badly weaken the ship and she would most likely leak very badly.

"My speculation about her was not idle, as Captain Percival informed us that the guns should be hoved overboard if she was in danger of sinking to ease her . . . ."]

Ship's ballast tanks
(Photo by Margie J. Shaw, courtesy of USN).

Chapter Two

The Indian Ocean Voyage

At Sea

Tuesday, October 15, 1844 -- Commences with fresh breezes and very pleasant weather. Around 4, the squalls came and we reduced sail to close reefed topsails. The mizzen topsail was furled and we sent down the royal yards. The courses were furled and the main trysail was set as we headed off the shore.

At 2 a.m., we wore ship to the east. At 4, a light reported on the lee bow. We soon discovered it to be a setting star. At 5 a.m., the trysail was "braised" [braced] up and set courses reefed. At 6, we turned the reefs out of the courses and set our topsails. [During this process, the ship's sail was taken up at reef points, and then the canvass was later turned out including the topsails to gather more wind.] At 8, we discovered land on our weather bow. We then turned out all reefs and made sail to royals, wind hauling aft. We set the studding sail. We hoved to and sounded in 70 fathoms of water. No bottom reported. At noon, we could all clearly spy land on our starboard bow. Water made in the hold these 24 hours 7 inches. Latitude 24.15 South/Longitude 43.35 East.

Off Sandy Island, Madagascar

October 16, 1844 -- We are presently standing along the shore of Madagascar, which is about 6 miles in the distance and to the eastward. We have sounded several times in from 15 to 20 fathoms. We bent the starboard cable as we passed Sandy Island. This island, though very low, may be called a good landmark. At the west end there is a small cluster of trees which appear to be the only vegetation on it. The rest of the island from the ship seems to be nothing more than a barren sandy spot. It is locked in by a reef of coral to the south and west, about 1/2 mile from shore. A heavy surf was breaking upon it as we passed. At 5:40 p.m., we clewed up all sail and came to with the starboard anchor in 7 fathoms of water and veered to the 40 fathoms chain. We took the following bearing: West End of Sandy Island, Southwest by South, the East End was Southwest by West 1/4 West, distance 1 and 1/4 miles from it. The entrance to St. Augustine was East 1/4 South and at a distance of 6 miles. We sent a boat with the Master, Mr. Strain, to sound around the ship and to draw attention of any natives who might have observed our anchorage. Midshipman Mason reported seeing something like smoke signals at a distance, but he was not definite of his observation. It is very likely though that the inhabitants have known of our coming several days in advance as it seems to be their nature or instinct.

Our clerk, Mr. Stevens, informed me of the ship's approach. Our course had been set for Port Crocker, as it was desired by Captain Percival to make the land below St. Augustine Bay. We then kept along the shore, being about four or five miles off Sandy Island. We then kept off from a quarter to three-quarters of a point east, and rounded Sandy Island at about a mile distant. The land all along the shore presented a barren aspect, and anyone who has seen Cape Henry or Sandy Hook, can judge the appearance of the coast.

During the latter part of that day, we furled sail with a reef taken in the topsail and by daylight, we sent 3rd. and 4th. cutters in charge of Lieutenant Grant and Master Strain from the ship towards the entrance of the Bay, to sound and make reports. From their reports, Captain Percival compared them with charts drawn by Captain W.F.W. Owens of the Royal Navy in the year 1824; they were found to be correct for anchorage positions within the Bay. We next stood for anchorage in St. Augustine Bay. Water made in the hold these 24 hours 5 inches.

At Saint Augustine Bay
Madagascar Island

October 17, 1844 -- At 4:40 p.m., we came to with the larboard anchor in 18 fathoms. "Tent Rock" had a bearing on compass South 1/2 West and Sandy Island West 3/4 South. We sent a boat to the French merchant Brig to ascertain what were the facilities for obtaining wood, water and fresh provisions and whether the natives were now very friendly to strangers. On the return of the boat, we found the answer to our questions as being very satisfactory.

We hoisted the 1st. cutter and launch and got the casks in them to bring back the badly needed fresh water. By the time our cutter left the ship, we could see the harbor filling with canoes from the shore. Our decks became almost too crowded to get any work done with curious natives. Among them we had the honor of meeting "Prince Green" [a self-appointed potentate].

He wore a very elaborate robe of state made up of the following: an old navy cap with a tarnished band of gold, a pepper and salt frock coat, an extremely dirty shirt, formerly belonging to some officer, and a pair of sailours' duck trowsers rolled up to the knees, and a black gin bottle in his pocket. All of this we heard he obtained from the U.S.S. Concord and John Adams. The people on deck may be classed with the darkest people that can be found in this world. We also heard that Prince Green owns Tent Rock.

Prince Green brought onboard his court as well. They were: John Green, his nephew and purser, John Stouts, his toady [manservant], Captain Amber, Captain Martin, and still others of his court.

John Green was styled in dress in the most original manner possible. An old tattered navy waistcoat, one epaulet, a sailor's hat, and various pieces of cotton composed his wardrobe. To crown the whole, he had an American eagle (brass) fastened onto his vest behind. He had only one eye, and on the whole was the most original looking officer that I have ever seen.

Most of the other men had nothing but strips of cotton crossing from shoulder to shoulder, to the hips and fastened around their loins. They soon found their way into steerage amongst the reefers, and quickly made use of the clothing given them. One fellow had a shirt given him, and a pair of drawers, which set tight to his legs, and with the aid of an old straw hat, was soon transformed into an apology of a well dressed man. With this finery, he was walking the quarterdeck as proud as any Turkish Bashaw with three tails. Another fellow was honored with the "Crown of

Neptune" [a ceremonial fake crown that the crew had made during their crossing at the equator].

Nearly all brought letters of recommendation from different whale ships which were not favorable to their honesty. One of them brought a letter signed "Sam Slick", stating the bearer to be a rascal and not trustworthy. Not being able to read, he had been gulled into taking it, and it would have done a person's heart good to see the look of approbation with which he received the letter again and carefully stowed it away, presuming, I suppose, that it bore testimony to his honesty.

I went on shore several times and was not much pleased with the visits. The people are beggars and robbers, and I was eased of my 'kerchief in a very short time. Dollars, buttons, beads, cloth, etc., are the articles of trade for which the natives give vegetables, fish, spears, etc. No cultivation was seen on this part of the island. The people live in bamboo huts not higher than themselves, and have to crawl in through a door, upon all fours. They appear to resemble pigsties more than the habitations of human beings. Tamarinds [a tropical fruit tree] grow wild near the river, where we obtained our water, and of these we picked a great quantity to take to sea.

They take a very palatable drink, which resembles lemonade. The main interest in St. Augustine is observing savage life; the natives are treacherous, and it would be dangerous to stay overnight amongst them. Two months of the year, January and February, the sickly season prevails.

The chief articles of export from St. Augustine are moss, used for dying, and dollars, which the natives receive from ships. Not much can be said of this harbor. The water is rather thick and muddy, and the wood is not the best; this place is really only good for whalers to visit. One thing we clearly learned was that the savages are far worse off now than before the while man introduced civilization amongst them.

[Midshipman Lucius Mason also recorded some personal observations about the native customs of St. Augustine:]

"The natives live in the most perfect simplicity. That is, they have a hand to mouth system of life. The greatest proportion of the population live almost entirely on vegetables, as only the very few wealthy among them eat meat.

"They live in small huts that are about 8 feet by 6 and about 4 feet high. The roof is raised over them about 4 feet higher. That is, the roof is about 8 feet from the ground. The huts are built of small poles interwoven with flags and rushes and roofed with the same. Both ends of the roof produce full apertures through which the smoke is allowed to escape from cooking. Somehow, the roof is perfectly water-proof.

"Living as they do on the seacoast, their canoes are a major concern with natives. The cross-sticks over the side are used to form an out-rigger to prevent the canoe from upsetting when carrying sail; the canoe itself being very narrow. They are about 15 feet long and about 18 inches wide. These out-riggers are always on the lee side, either end will do for the head. These out-riggers do not answer as well as those used by the natives of the south Pacific. When I observed the Africans, their boats have a problem by being always on the lee side. They always rest on the water, and of course the harder it blows, the deeper they are buried, thus impeding their headway very much. Because of this there is too much rudder effect, and the drag motion brings the boat gradually around in a circular direction. In order to counter act this, the natives are constantly having to keep a paddle out on the opposite side with the broad part against the water in order to keep the canoe going in a straight course.

"Their religion consists of a sort of mixed paganism and Mohometism. What I learned of it, I got from a watch from 8 to midnight. Johnny Green stayed with me and walked the decks talking of his form of worship. He said that the only night of Mohometism is very special and that they undergo circumcision that night. They are very strict in their religious views, even though they let the more physical niceties as washing go. Nearly all of them carry various charms around their necks. They call the charms Mahomets. The Mahomets are made of various things such as bits of wood, nails of animals, the teeth of alligators, and indeed almost anything they can get. I asked Johnny Green about his Mahomet. He said the real importance of them was that if he was to die with his Mahomet around his neck, he would almost certainly go to heaven, but that if he lost it, and then died, they would not go to heaven.

"There are too many religious ceremonies of the natives to account for in this short account. One of the ones I observed more closely was their burial of their dead. I noticed that Johnny Green's hair was shaved close to his head. He said that he had this done in religious rites after his father had died. He had also killed 120 bullock sheep, 10 sheep, 10 herfers [sic], and 10 goats. I asked him if he killed any chickens to sacrifice. Green then told me that he had buried them near his father so that he might have food to eat. He also buried a spear along with his father so that he might go hunting in the after-world. They also buried their dead with the head facing East.

"A system of counting had also been developed by them. It relates directly to all other civilized forms. I took pains to learn it; esta - 1, cua - 2, tello - 3, effa - 4, leema - 5, suna - 6, feeto - 7, vallo - 8, sheeva - 9, faola - 10, and so on. These are

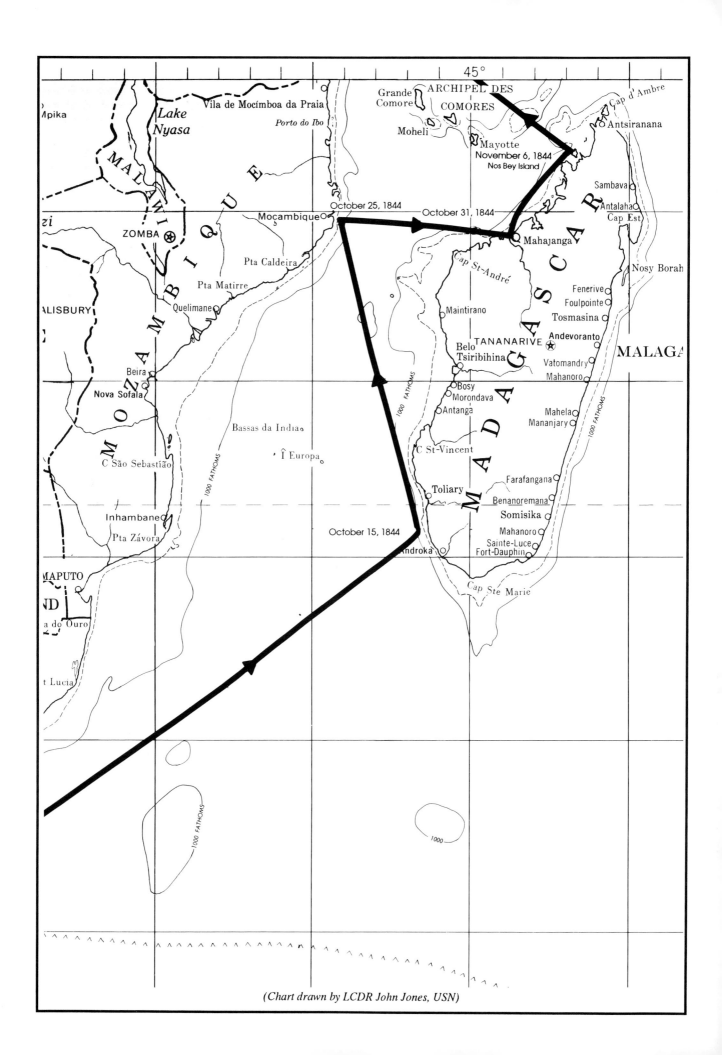

(Chart drawn by LCDR John Jones, USN)

their numbers up to ten and then a very wide deviation begins. For brevity, I will not list them all here."]

October 18, 1844 -- Commences with light breezes from the north and east and clear pleasant weather. At 3 p.m., we hoisted the 2nd. cutter. We received on board by the launch 1800 gallons of water and a quantity of wood.

At 9 a.m., sent the wood and water party with the launch and 1st. cutter under the charge of Master Strain up the Dartmouth River, which is situated about 4 miles from the anchorage. In going up this river, we had a pilot who called himself "Johnny Greene", a one-eyed native, in the launch. In the 1st cutter another pilot was called "Johnny Stouts."

These fellows seemed to command some respect from the natives that crowded about the boats wherever we landed. The natives, further up the river, are very fond of trading and begging jacknives, brass buttons and coarse stuff. They will purchase anything that is wished and so these were in plenty with the crew. They passed their time most pleasantly with the natives. Virtues they have none. Steal they will if they have a chance. To all appearances they are not a treacherous race of beings and from what I saw I think they are truly a friendly race to Americans. They express a great dislike to the Spanish and Portuguese and speak often of their relatives that have been stolen by them and sold into slavery. In the Dartmouth River, creek would be a better name, there is coral and bars which are hazards to boat traffic. The wood is obtained along the bank of the river and is very good indeed. Bullocks sheep [male] and vegetables such as potatoes, beans, and pumpkins, may be found here in abundance.

October 18, 1844 -- We received on board another 1800 gallons of water, a quantity of wood, and three Bullocks sheep. I would now like to enter a short history of Madagascar from Abbe Rouhou's voyage to Madagascar and the East Indies: The island of Madagascar was discovered in 1506, by Lawrence Almeyda, but the Persians and Arabs knew it from time immemorial under the name of Sarandib. Alphonse Albuguerque commissioned Ruy Percisa of Conthentha to explore the interior part. He ordered Tristan d'Acunha to sail around it and mark the bearings of its principal capes and head lands. It is divided into 23 provinces.

When the Portuguese discovered this island they wished to give it the name of St. Lawrence. In the reign of Henry VI, the French named it "Ile Dauphine," although its real name is Madagcasse, it is generally known under that of Madagascar. According to several learned geographers, this island is the Cerne of Pling, and the

Minuthiasde of Ptolemy [Here Thomas refers to the ancient names of the island which evidence his education in classical geography and history.]

It extends almost north northeast and south southwest and lies between 12 and 26 degrees of south latitude. We may reckon that the superficies of this island contain two hundred million acres of land, watered on all sides by streams and large rivers.

October 19, 1844 -- The forests contain a prodigious variety of the most beautiful trees, such as palm, ebony, etc. Dye woods, bamboo of enormous size, orange and lemon, timber fit for masts and constructing ships are no less common. There are doubtless few countries in the world where navigators can find in greater abundance, and at less expense, refreshments of every kind.

October 20, 1844 -- We have busily employed taking on board hardwood and water. At 4:30, we got the boats in and unmoored the ship. At 6, we hoved to 45 fathoms chain. At 4:40, we hoved short and loosed sail. Crossed topgallants and royal yards. At 5, we got underway and made sail, standing out to sea.

We discovered a sail in the offing. At 10 a.m., we got a breeze from the south and west. We set the courses and spanker and tacked to the north and west. The crew was inspected at quarters. We have had only 35 men on the sick list and that was during the doubling of the Cape, and there are less now. At 11:30, we hoved to and lowered the 3rd. cutter and sent it alongside the H.B.M. Brig of War Sappho. The cutter was directed by Lt. Paine. He brought the Captain of the brig over to visit. We ascertained that the Sappho was from Quillaman [Coast of Africa] bound on a cruise. At 11:40, we returned the cutter and parted company. On our own course, Sandy Island was bearing compass South by West 1/2 West. The distance was 15 miles. The ship is now under plain sail.

[Thomas must have had access to the ship's library and was aware of Constitution's role in correcting earlier surveys as he copied the following in his journal.]

[Extracts from the Journal of W.F.W. Owen (British Vice-Admiral, who, under the sponsorship of the Royal Geographical Society, explored the west African coasts in 1821) while embarked on a surveying expedition, 1824, in the H.B.M. Ships Leven and Barracouda:]

"The coast from St. Augustine to Boganna Bay is almost an Unvaried low, marshy plain, irrigated by rivers. It is bounded by a line of sharp pointed coral masses, uncovered when the tide is low and in two or three places there are a couple of archipelago or rocky islet, running in a variety of whimsical shapes. The shore is thinly covered with trees of a stunted growth. The coral islet and reefs that skirt the coast are very numerous and to those acquainted with them are extremely dangerous. The islands all along the coast are low and formed of coral and seldom exceeding one mile in circumference. It should also be remarked that the reef that runs along the coast runs to the southward."

At Sea

October 25, 1844 -- During these 24 hours, we made and reduced sail as the situation demanded. We found by a meridian aft of the star Orion, the latitude to be 14.51 degrees South. We experienced fast currents in this area, and discovered a northerly current of 27 miles up to 4 a.m. At 5, we discovered land off our weather bow about 15 miles in the distance. At 7:30, we took on our studdingsail [an additional sail usually set in fine weather, with the wind abaft--toward the stern--the beam; they are set by extending the yards with booms], and braced sharp up. At 9, we were working for the harbor of Mozambique. This portion of the African coast is really beautiful. There are trees of great height. They appear like magic to rise from the sea. The land is very low and cannot be seen until you get very near it. There is a heavy surf breaking all along the coast. Water made in the hold these 24 hours 4 inches. Latitude 15.15 South/Longitude 40.55 East.

[According to the letterbook of Midshipman Lucius Mason, the Constitution was fortunate to have made this passage:

"The last time we tacked off shore, we were very near the northern point [St. Jago, an island 3 miles off Mozambique] running some distance into the sea. The men were somewhat fatigued, and at this point they began to work badly.

"Just as the sails got aback in swinging the yards around, the wind which had been rather light before, freshened up very much. The wind pressed the sails against the masts so as to cause the yards to be swung with a great deal of difficulty. The consequence was that she came very near not going about on the other tack and if she had missed going about, she would according to judgement, have gone ashore.

"There would have been no alternative, for I am sure we were not a full cables length from the rocks. If an anchor or a dozen anchors had been cast over, it would have been of no use. With all the sails we had on her, she would have dragged a dozen more anchors. We did not have time to take in the sails either. At any other time, we would have surely touched the shore, but oh, not the Constitution. Her guardian angel had not left her to peril on the burning rocks and sand of Mozambique, for go about she did, and the brave action was smartly done."]

Harbor of Mozambique

October 26, 1844 -- This day commenced with a moderate breeze and pleasant weather. We are now beating up the harbor of Mozambique [on the east coast of Africa] on the inshore tack, approaching inshore little more than a quarter of a mile. At 7:30, the current was pulling against us and some wind ahead. We finally came to with the larboard anchor in 10 fathoms; we were off St. Iago, Island. We veered to with the 50 fathom chain. The compass bearing is Northwest by North, and the South end of St. Iago had a compass bearing West. During the remainder of this day, the winds and weather were fresh.

At 8 a.m., we commenced kedging [using the kedge anchors to maneuver the ship] and cleared the reef of St. Iago. The harbor we entered is formed by a deep inlet of the sea. It is about five miles broad and about six miles in length, receiving the waters of three major rivers. When entering the port, two small islands may be observed nearly surrounded by a reef of coral rocks and sand bars, which render any approach very difficult to make.

The outer islands are St. Iago [St. Jago] and St. George, the former to the south and the later to the north, laying ahead of each other at the distance of about a cable length or two and a distance of about 3 miles from Mozambique. Wood and water may be obtained here, but the conveyances are so very bad that it would be advisable for ships not to attempt it, but rather over at the island of Mozambique. There one may find wood, water, beef, and vegetables in great abundance. Everything is at a dirt cheap price. The town of Mozambique is under Portuguese authority and from appearances is fortified. The streets of this place are very narrow and nothing else but sandy roads. The houses are from one to two stories high and built of stone, then white washed over. The lower classes live in bamboo huts, which in this climate, I would think much cooler than the other type.

We also received two officers onboard from the Portuguese government. We asked them to take a note to the Governor. In the afternoon, they returned with a pilot so that we could re-draw several of our charts of the area. The pilot also had a letter from His Excellency Brigadier General R.L. d'Abun d'Luria, Governor General of Mozambique.

October 27, 1844 -- At 4:30, we hoisted the Portuguese flag and fired a salute of 21 guns. Our salute was returned. Before anyone left the ship, it was Captain Percival's idea that all punishments must be handed out. Many times the scenes are too gruesome to make record of them. The pity of it all was that the men punished were constantly getting back in trouble and their bodies soon carried the marks of their bad characters. That day Joseph Sinnett, seaman, was given many lashes of the colt for general disobedience of orders and J.R. Heard was punished with 6 lashes of the colt [length of rope knotted at the end] for neglect of duty. We also pumped the ship as we make an average of 4 inches of water every 24 hours.

Captain Percival and a group of officers went to the city and called upon the Governor. The General received the Captain with great courtesy and expressed a great desire to have the frigate nearer the city for viewing. He explained the views of the Portuguese government towards that of the United States of America and evidenced much interest in the commercial transactions of our country. It appears that whalers frequently send in boats for wood and water, but rarely visit the city. A steady and lucrative trade is carried on between Salem and New York and Mozambique. The Brig Richmond, from New York, and the Brig Emmerton, from Salem, are the only two vessels regularly trading. The exports are ivory, gums, copal [a resin], etc., for which they receive cotton, etc. in exchange. It being made manifest to the Captain that our commerce was not suffering at this port, he took leave of the Governor.

Ship's Clerk Stevens was very pleased with his visit to the city of Mozambique. He stated very aptly that even though he would not describe the city as beautiful, it was though a great example of Portuguese splendor and grandeur. Portugal, at the time of its taking possession of this island, must have been an enterprising nation.

The fort, a part of which is occupied, is capable of mounting 300 guns, and commands the harbor and coast of Africa. It was built in the year 1511. The Governor's house was built by the Jesuits, and is the handsomest place in the city. Near it stands an old convent in a state of decay, and, in fact, all the buildings seem to be so, though most are inhabited. The city contains about 200 whites, 1,500 negroes, and a few Arabs, who may be seen walking the streets in their native costumes, apparently regardless of the wonder bestowed upon them.

What could have induced the Portuguese to make a settlement in this sickly climate I cannot conceive, unless it was the idea that they had discovered the "Philosopher's Stone" [an imaginary stone or preparation believed to have the power of transmuting the baser [sic] metals into gold, much sought after by alchemists] on the coast of Africa, and wanted a commanding post to overlook the scene of action. Immense quantities of slaves are said to be exported annually to Brazil from this island. The negroes are brought from the interior of Africa and sold by their own countrymen to the traders in this inhuman traffic. But the resources that Mozambique was said to possess are fast dwindling away. Its port is of hard entrance. Trade which formerly was confined to this island has been extended along the coast from the Cape of Good Hope to the equator, and slavery particularly, one of its greatest sources of revenue, has met the disapprobation of European powers.

These causes, combined together with the port affording no fresh provisions, etc., are continually operating to render Mozambique of less importance as a city than other places along the coast. The enterprise of the Portuguese government has flagged, and Mozambique can now only present a vivid picture of what we must suppose to have once been a powerful and well fortified port, capable of maintaining itself from aggression by land or sea. But, alas for poor Portugual, the days of prosperity are over, and that success no longer awaits it which made it the first of nations in the time of Vasco da Gama.

At Sea

October 29, 1844 -- At 1:15, we wore ship, and lowered a boat to ascertain whether or not we had a current. We found it running around 1/2 knot West South West on the compass. Thomas Glavin and Thomas Williams were punished with 6 lashes of the colt each for skulking below during their watch.

At 10:00 p.m., we saw a large meteor and another one following close to the south. At the time we were still in the Mozambique Channel. We were heading for Bombetoka, Madagascar. The sky was clear when we were all alerted by the meteor's passage. The moon was at half. The meteor presented an unusual light of blue, tinged with red. It was first observed nearly above the ship, and descended, until near the horizon it disappeared. We have all seen what are called shooting stars, but this meteor did not resemble any we have ever seen in shape or color. It did not appear to be very far away from us as its passage lit up the entire ship including the rigging.

It should be noticed that at day's end, 7:30, we observed the punishment of Lott Green, cockpit steward, for stabbing Thomas Pusey with his knife. Green was given 12 lashes of the cat o'nine tails.

October 31, 1844 -- At 5:30, the crew was inspected at quarters. During the last dog watch [either of the two watches between 4 pm and 8 pm], lightening was observed to the south and west. At 8, we sounded in 22 fathoms of water. The bottom was fine, white sand, and some shells. At 8:15, we sounded in 20 fathoms of water; the bottom was a coarse black sand. We reduced the sail to top gallant sails. We sounded during the nights with the hand lead in from 13 to 20 fathoms of water.

At 4 a.m., we passed over a shoal carrying 7 fathoms of water. It should be noted that this shoal is not laid down on the charts of Captain W.F.W. Owens of the Royal Navy. At 9 a.m., we exercised the crew at general quarters. At 9:30, the ship was tacked. Water made in the hold these 24 hours 4 inches. Distance made 64 miles. Latitude 15.32 South/Longitude 45.08 East.

Town of Majunga
Bombetoka Bay, Madagascar

November 2, 1844 -- At 1:30, shortened sail and backed the main topsail up to the foresail. At 2, filled away and all hands were called to work ship. Master Strain was sent in one of the cutters ahead to test the current.

At 4, we entered the Bay of Bombetoka [can be found on the northwest side of Madagascar, now the Republic of Malagasy]. At 5, clewed up the topsails and came to with the larboard anchor in 7 fathoms of water. Veered to with the 40 fathoms chain. Furled the sail. We then took the following bearing by the flagstaff in the town of Majunga. It bore NNE 1/2 E. Lambingo Hill bore N 3/4 E. Napanjara Point lay NW by W 1/4 W. At sunset, the top gallant was sent down and the royal yards were done likewise. Eugene Scully was given 9 lashes for sleeping by the drift lead.

November 2, 1844 -- The town of Majunga is situated on the Northeast side and at the entrance of the Bay of Bombetoka. Back of the town, there is an excuse of a fort. The greater part of the battery was consisting of guns obtained from trading ships on the coast. They are all of old ages and various sizes. By examining one specimen of an 18 lb. long gun, they seem to be the survivors of the original battery of Noah's Ark.

November 4, 1844 -- The Captain allowed 29 men to go ashore. They were to be at liberty until sunset. At sunset, some returned, most of whom were very drunk with the effects of rum. The officers were alerted of the affairs onshore. Meanwhile onboard, we took 1400 gallons of water.

Most of the water was hardly fit, being very dirty. At 8 a.m., we loosed the sail to allow it to dry from the light rain we had. We fired a salute of 4 guns, which was returned by Captain Percival and men who had gone to visit the fort. They were officially inspecting the fortifications and defense work, making notes of all they saw or heard. Secondly, a number of crewmen had not returned after liberty. It was certain onboard that a minor mutiny was about to take place, without any apparent reason for the mischief.

November 5, 1844 -- We received onboard 4 bullocks and 1400 gallons of water. Captain Percival remarked, when he came onboard, that there had been some trouble with the men who had broken liberty, and that seaman Edward Brett had threatened him when they attempted to bring the men back. Finally after a small fight, the seamen were brought back. Shortly after, all hands were called to witness the punishment of the 12 leaders. They were each given 12 lashes or more for their activity in the matter. Some still seemed to be drunk at the time of punishment, but the Captain made sure all were sober after.

[Ship's Clerk B.F. Stevens described Majunga and Bombetoka:

"Majunga is situated on the Northwest coast of Madagascar, and is one of the principal seaports. The Queen of the island has erected a fort on the hill in the center of the town, and a garrison of native soldiers is placed in it. The town is mostly occupied by Malagash and Arabs, and is the most civilized place we have seen as yet. The trade of Majunga is in hides, horns, etc., for which is exchanged clothes and fancy articles. Several American vessels from Salem, Massachusetts regularly take cargoes from here, and an agent for the owner, David Pengree, resides in the town at present.

"The town of Bombetoka lies farther up the bay, and is not of so much importance as Majunga. Formerly, in King Radama's time, a considerable trade was carried on with both places, principally in hides and jerked beef. Bombetoka Bay takes in the whole from the sea side to the mouth of the rivers, and is very beautiful and large. But the depth of water will not allow a draft of much more than 24 feet.

"The people seem more civilized and educated than those in the southern end. A regular currency has been established with the use of chiseled pieces of silver. The trade with the Hindoos seems to be of great interest to everyone, since they are now penetrating into the interior of the island, most of which is yet to be explored. There is an American representative of Salem here named Marks. He has apparently been doing rather well for himself except for the rumor that there are Black Marks as well.

"I now come to my most interesting circumstance during my visit to the Town of Madagascar. I was shown an awful evidence that the crimes of robbery, arson, etc., are most severely punished. It appears that three natives had burned and robbed the storehouse of Mr. Vincent Marks, the agent for the American merchants that I mentioned previously. They were discovered and condemned to the flames, their heads to be stuck upon poles on the beach as a warning to others who might feel disposed to appropriate their neighbor's goods to their own use. One of these skulls was yet to be seen on a pole, while the others had fallen to the ground. It had remained up for six months; the hair was still visible. Two of the skulls were smuggled onboard without notice. They will no doubt adorn some reefer's studio at the termination of the cruise."]

November 6, 1844 -- We then sailed on a northerly course to the island of Nos Bey [Nosy-be island is on the extreme northwest coast of the Malagasy Republic]. We anchored near the town of Passandava. The island lies at the mouth of Passandava Bay. It is about twelve miles in length and four to five miles in width. Our scientist (Dr. Reinhardt) states that it is most likely volcanic in origin.

We were the first American man-of-war to have ever visited Nos Bey, and the natives were very curious of the Constitution. Nos Bey is still in the possession of the French. They have built a fort upon it and stationed a garrison of soldiers from the Isle de Bourbon. The small islands of Mayotte, St. Mary's, and Nos Bey are all under French protection. Nos Bey is far the prettiest island of the group and the most beautiful place we have visited next to Rio de Janeiro. It bears a strong resemblance to the West Indies, except for its lack of civilization.

Nos Bey was formerly a possession of the Sakalava tribe. About five years ago, the French bought it; ever since then, great exertions have been made to civilize the natives, but without much success. There are also many Arabs who live on the island. They have formed a village of their own a short distance from the main settlements. The Arabs use a small boat, or dhow, to trade with the natives. The dhows are about the size of a coasting sloop. There are also many Bombay merchants living here; trade is surely to increase as will the importance of the island.

We are told that the native population of Sakalavas is around 15,000. The French seem to be disliked a great deal by the natives as they act in a despotic way. The obvious plan of the French is to gain control over the Island of Madagascar, and, with the islands of Mayotte and Nos Bey on the west of it and St. Mary's on the east, all of which can be well fortified, its chance of success is great.

I need to make note that the French were very un-cooperative in securing our supplies. No one onboard knew of any reason for this, but there was surely no doubt of their unfriendly behavior. We made record that it was very evident that the French are trying in all their power to take over the islands. They have stationed influential agents in the capital to better influence the Queen. Whether this is a direct plan of the

French Government is not known, but they have as noted usurped the power and influence of Great Britain. On the morning of November 12, we weighed anchor and headed for our next destination, Zanzibar [off the coast of what is now Tanganyika].

Off Zanzibar Island

November 13, 1844 -- At 3 p.m., the eastern point of Zanzibar Island bore a compass reading of Southwest by South 1/2. We could also point out Pemba Island. The coast of Africa is in sight. We are standing in for the wester end of the island. At 5:30, all hands were called to bring the ship to anchor. At 6, we took in all sails and came too with the kedge in 12 fathoms of water. We had a sandy bottom. The sails were soon furled. A letter was sent in to the American Consul in Zanzibar at our arrival. The message was carried by a native in one of their small dhows [usually one-masted sail boat with oars, normally used for fishing, but larger ones, 20-feet or more could be armed with small cannon for piracy]. When standing in for the island, it was ascertained that there was a strong current setting 1/2 knot per hour to the east.

At 5 a.m., all hands were called to make sail and hove up the kedge. We next stood around the north point of Zanzibar. At 8:40, all hands were called to witness the punishment of the deserters during our visit to Madagascar. Edward Brett, the leader, was flogged with 12 lashes of the cat for attempting to strike Captain Percival during the discussions to come back to the ship.

Captain Percival realized that Brett, although a trouble maker, was popular with the crew, so he read the charges against Brett himself and also the language and threats he made against Captain Percival and the ship. Captain Percival had to explain to the crew that a threat against the Captain is also a threat against the ship and can never be tolerated. The following language was used by Brett:

"Old Jack is a son-of-a-bitch and not much of a man. He struck me and I'll knock him down if I get a chance. He can punish me if he wishes, because I don't give a damn. I'll strike him if I get a chance and Jesus Christ himself will not be able to protect him."

The time that Brett made these remarks, he was in a sober condition and deserved the fair treatment he received back onboard. In a short while, all seemed forgotten and we never heard the Captain bring up the matter again.

Off Zanzibar

November 19, 1844 -- We received a pilot as directed by the American Consul. The next morning early we got underway and stood up for the city. The airs were light and the weather was pleasant. By 2:10, the wind was coming out of the south and east with light rain. We used our studding sails and braced up on the larboard tack under royals and flying jib. At 3:40, the town of Zanzibar was in sight.

We could see several vessels lying in at anchorage. We sounded with the hand lead in 17 fathoms of water. There was a hard muddy bottom. At 4:40, a gun was fired and the jack was hoisted. At 5 p.m., all hands were called to bring the ship to anchor. At 5:30, under the pilot's direction, we clewed up and came to with the larboard anchor in 8 fathoms of water off Metoni. Veered to by the 27 fathom chain.

The following bearings were taken off the City of Zanzibar; the fort in the city of Zanzibar bore Southwest 1/2 South, the arsenal at Metoni bore Southeast by South. At sundown, we sent the royals down, and the top gallant yards. At 7:30, the 1st. and 2nd. cutters were hoisted out. To our astonishment, no sooner than we arrived did we receive a barge commission by the Sultan of Muscat. The barge contained gifts to the Constitution consisting of 2 cows and 7 goats and a large assortment of fruit. The Captain was much pleased at the generosity of the Sultan's gift.

Running colors (Photo by Margie J. Shaw, courtesy of USN).

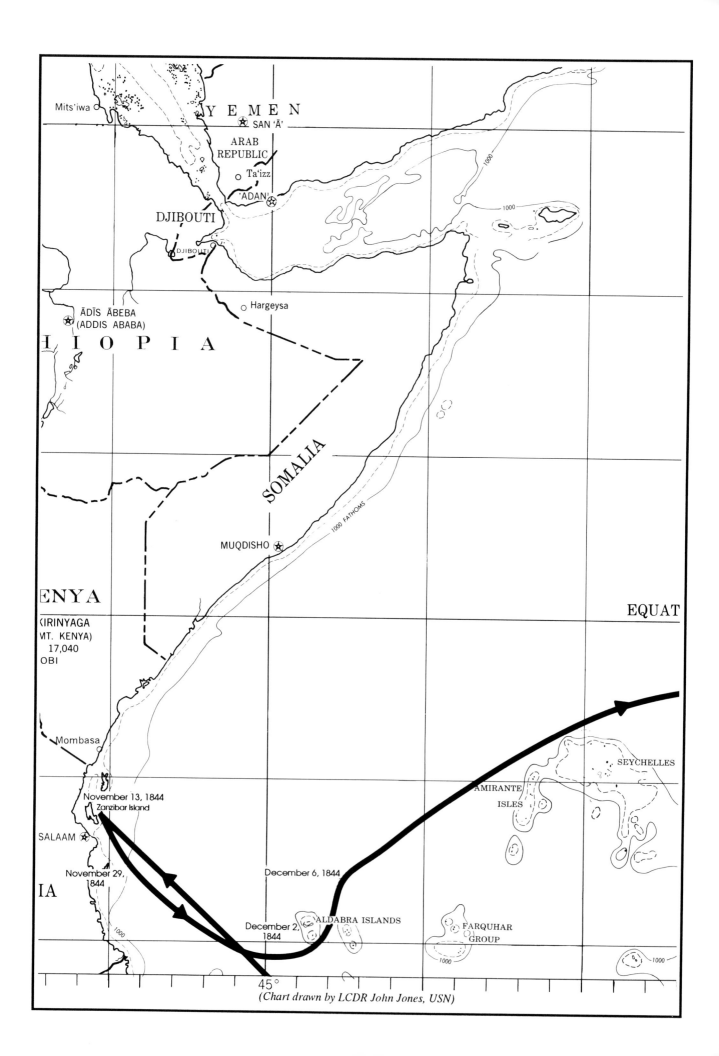

Mits'iwa

Y E M E N
☆ SAN 'Ā'
ARAB
REPUBLIC
Ta'izz
'ADAN' ☆

DJIBOUTI

DJIBOUTI

ĀDĪS ĀBEBA
(ADDIS ABABA)
☆

Hargeysa

H I O P I A

SOMALIA

MUQDISHO ☆

1000

1000

1000

1000 FATHOMS

ENYA

KIRINYAGA
MT. KENYA)
17,040
OBI

EQUAT

Mombasa

SEYCHELLES

AMIRANTE
ISLES

November 13, 1844
Zanzibar Island

SALAAM ☆

December 6, 1844

November 29,
1844

December 2,
1844

ALDABRA ISLANDS

FARQUHAR
GROUP

IA

1000

1000

1000

45°

(Chart drawn by LCDR John Jones, USN)

The island of Zanzibar is about 25 miles from the coast of Africa, and is about 40 miles in length and ten in breadth. The eastern side is formed of coral and reefs which extend out at least a mile from shore, while the western side is fertile, with a beautiful sandy beach. The appearance of the island is low and level. As we passed down towards the city immense groves of coconut trees met our sight; also another kind of tree which appeared to be under cultivation. This we later found out to be a clove tree from which the Sultan derives an annual income of $100,000.

The harbor of Zanzibar is extremely beautiful and large. We had been led to believe that there was grave danger in navigating this bay, but none was found. One but had to have a slight diligence and some degree of talent to command so large a vessel as this upon entering a strange harbor. Thus far on the coasts of Madagascar and Africa, the coastal surveys of Captain Owens have usually been very correct.

We also received onboard this day the American Consul Waters of Salem, Massachusetts. He was accompanied by one of the Sultan's officers, and the commanders of the French Corvette Berceau and an English Brig of sixteen guns. The island of Zanzibar, as well as all of those north of it are in the possession of the Sultan of Muscat. At present he resides here. Generally his representation is one of high character and a great degree of intelligence. The first of the Sultan's vessels to have ever visited the United States, the Sultani, is here out of commission. Water made in the hold these 24 hours is 4 inches.

Harbor of Zanzibar

November 20, 1844 -- At 1, we saluted the American Consul Waters with 7 guns after he spent a pleasant overnight onboard ship. At 3:30, we saluted the English Consul on leaving the ship with 9 guns. At 4:10, the French Commodore visited the ship and was saluted with 13 guns as he left for shore. The Captain grumbled at a continued day of diplomatic exchanges. The 1st. cutter was employed watering the ship [collecting fresh water for ship's tanks or storage].

The only fault in the water here is that it has been found to run directly beneath the Sultan's Palace and is not as clear as we should wish. Captain Owens attributes all the sickness onboard his vessels to this water. As yet we have found it good.

On the 20th., a party of officers accepted an invitation to dine with the Sultan.

[The following account of the visit was made by Captain Clerk Stevens:

"Accordingly at the appointed time we went to the palace, and were received at the gate by the Sultan himself. He was accompanied by his sons and grandsons. He appeared to be about sixty years of age. His beard, which descended half way down his breast, was gray, and altogether, he could be called a fine looking man. His dress was very plain, but neat, and differed little from the chiefs around him.

"He shook hands with the officers and seemed very pleased at the visit paid to him. He then led the way into the dining room, and after our Consul, Mr. Waters, had spoken a few words of congratulations to him, through the interpreter, we sat down to our feast.

"Our host did not sit with us, nor did he eat with us, but instead occupied a settee with his principal officers. We were waited upon by the eunuchs and other household staff. To attempt to describe the viands [courses] would be an impossibility since no two were exactly alike. What attracted the most attention was their arrangement.

"Plates were piled high, one atop the other, and the tables seemed to be groaning with their weight. Three goats roasted whole and two sheep curried whole formed the principal items. About twelve of us were present, and there must have been enough rice for a ship's company. It was useless to count the chickens and other types of fowl that the Sultan had ordered served for our feast. In all of our travels, all the officers agreed that this was the most magnificent feast of their lives.

"To end the meal a various assortment of pastries and fruit were served. But the richest treat to me was the sherbet. It is made of rose water and honey, and is a most delicious drink, but when much used, leaves a sickening taste in the mouth. It was as clear as the best spring water, and each person had a decanter before him. The interpreter called it Mohammedan's grog and I thought it a great pity that the Christian grog was not as harmless.

"After dining and shaking hands again with the Sultan we left and walked through his grounds as he was pleased to ask us to do. Immense groves of coconut trees are seen everywhere in the neighborhood of the palace, and the clove trees likewise. Never having seen either of these two useful articles growing, I was much pleased with the walk. Pineapples are also frequently met with."]

November 22, 1844 -- Captain Percival and another party of officers have left the ship to visit the Sultan. Once again all returned with the highest praise for his abilities in the art of hospitality. His highness definitely has a partiality for the Americans. This is owing to their unostentatious attitude for the fact that the Americans have not fortified the islands in the Mozambique Channel as the French and other nations have done.

At Zanzibar we found several Americans who are agents for Salem merchants. They carry on a lucrative trade in ivory and gum copal. Our Vice-Consul, Mr. Waters, and Captain John F. Webb did everything to render our stay as comfortable as possible. It has been gratifying to have stayed here. We all wish that the many other ports that we are to stop in will be as friendly as Zanzibar.

[Midshipman Lucius Mason summarized the condition of the African slave market at Zanzibar in the last section of his letterbook:

"The negro here, as in all other slave marts, is a miserable and unfortunate being. No one pities him, and no one feels for him, excepting strangers, who have no means of assisting him. A tear must drop by everyone who will reflect upon the degraded condition of his fellow being and think what a curse was inflicted upon this world by slavery."

[Thomas journal continues:]

Harbor of Zanzibar

November 24, 1844 -- We are busy preparing the ship for our next destination which will be the Island of Sumatra. The crossing of the Indian Ocean can be a long one, but there is talk of more accurate chartings on currents and dependable wind currents shortening the distance a great amount.

Since it was Sunday, Captain Percival read the sermon. At 10:00 in the morning, all hands were called to muster at the morning prayer. The sermon read was Lazarus and the Rich Man, being one of the Captain's favorites.

November 26, 1844 -- Today we received onboard one bullock sheep. The 1st. cutter is ashore watering for the next voyage. We also once again received gifts from the Sultan; this time we were presented with a quantity of excellent wood.

At 2:00 a.m., most of the crew including the Captain stayed up for a total eclipse of the moon. What a romantic sight it was so far from home and in such exotic waters.

The next morning had hardly begun before we received more gifts of fresh fruit from the Sultan. All on board have been very pleased at the great amount of hospitality given him to the entire crew.

Perhaps Zanzibar has been too friendly as there is some talk among the men of a large number of deserting vessels here and hoping to ship home with the next passing vessel in the opposite direction. We have had but two, and their whereabouts on the island are already known; they are John White and William Jones. Most of the deserters will volunteer for cutter duty and while filling the tanks will sneak off. Most of that type can be found frequently at the same bar where they were last seen the previous night and many are returned in the most vile condition. We now have a published sick list; there are 13 crewmen on it.

November 27, 1844 -- We finished all preparations for sea. The last dingy was hoisted in. At 3:30 p.m., we fired a gun and hoisted the cornet. We then received our pilot. At 3:45, we made sail to topgallant, weighed anchor and stood out the harbor. The H.M.C.M. Corvette Berceau was in our company. At 5:40, we shortened the sail and clewed up. At 6, the sails were furled and we let go the kedge in 21 fathoms of water. We veered by the 30 fathoms howser. The pilot and the American Consul left the ship and returned to Zanzibar. Our two deserters were also captured and were said to be detained at the Consul's quarters. We waited for them to be returned. They soon returned when the American Consul reached shore and their punishment can soon be expected onboard. The kedge was soon thereafter weighed and we made sail with royals and flying jib. The coast of Africa is still in sight on our weather beam. Sick report now 16.

November 28, 1844 -- Commenced with light and pleasant weather. At 3, we got the sea breeze from the east southeast. At 4, we were standing for the African shore. The southern point of Zanzibar bore South by West 1/2 West. We made and reduced sail as was required. At 3:40, we found no bottom with a 38 fathom line. At 8:40, we at last sounded in 24 fathoms of water. There was a very rocky bottom, perhaps at one point in history there might have been some volcanic activity in the area. All hands were called and the ship came too with the kedge in 23 fathoms of water and veered in 50 fathoms. Latham Island bore Southeast by South 1/2 at a distance of 36 miles from Zanzibar. Having some interest in this region, our scientist joined the Captain, clerk and several others who went ashore.

[Ship's Clerk Stevens wrote the following report of their visit to Latham Island:

"A boat was sent ashore to gather guano. From the ship, through a glass, millions of birds could be seen. Evidently they were not pleased at the first visit. Our boat returned carrying several bags of guano and a few strange birds, some of whom resemble the eider duck.

"The island was entirely covered with guano to the depth of a foot or more. It is about a quarter of a mile in length and is rocky at the eastern side, and sandy at the west. Its foundation is coral. The birds did not relish the intrusion and several men were sent back to the boat with badly bitten hands. They appeared crazy when several men fired their guns. None, however, were shot as it was so easy to capture them with the hand.

"The island was discovered in 1758 by the East India Company ship Latham and is only 10 feet above sea level. In the present state of things, fortune might be easily made by taking the guano for agricultural purposes. At twelve, we weighed the kedge and kept on our course."]

At Sea

November 29, 1844 -- At 2 p.m., we discovered a shoal about 3 points on our lee bow; another directly ahead. We sent two boats ahead with officers to examine them and place their position on the chart. Latham Island bore east by west at a distance of 2 miles. At 4:30, there was some gunnery practice and the cornet was hoisted. At 5 p.m., the boats returned. No charts give any position to these shoals. At sunset, Latham Island bore north at a distance of 8 miles. Sounding in 9 fathoms of water as the island is out of sight. The sick report now lists 20 men. Latitude 7.32 south/Longitude 40.35 east.

December 2, 1844 -- At 5:30, the crew was inspected at quarters. At 2:45, we hit a very violent squall with heavy lightning and thunder with torrents of rain. The ship was reduced to plain sail [sail of reduced size, alternately a fore-and-aft sail set on the mast of a square-rigged ship.] At 8 a.m., all hands were called to witness the punishment and flogging of John White and William Jones. They were reported and caught in desertion in Zanzibar. The Captain informed the crew that they had also resisted arrest by the Zanzibar police. The American Consul had asked the police to apprehend the two characters. Also, while White and Jones were in desertion, a fellow crew member, John Collins, had been caught searching through their clothes. Each of them were punished by 12 lashes of the cat. Sick report has 29 men. Latitude 10.15 south/Longitude 44.44 east.

At Sea

[The following report was written by Ship's Clerk B.F. Stevens, December 6, 1844:

"We are now about 10 days from Zanzibar. The weather is beautiful, and I am sitting at the cabin port, writing letters home to my friends. The thermometer is 82 degrees in the shade and I suppose in Boston it is below zero. Today might be considered one of the most pleasant days we have spent during the entire voyage. Old

Ironsides moves along with good speed as usual. If old Mr. Humphries [Joshua Humphries of Philadelphia was her original designer] were to see her now he would hardly know her. She is painted lead color, with a bright red streak, and "Old Andrew" [bow figure carved in the likeness of President Andrew Jackson] at the prow is in fancy colors. Altogether, I think Old Ironsides and Joseph's coat would have been two great curiosities. The following sketch of the day will give one some idea of the usual routine on board a man-of-war.

"At daylight, the spar and gun decks are scrubbed and washed and dry by 7 o'clock. At that time all hammocks are stowed and hammock clothes drawn neatly over. At 8, the boys are mustered and examined by the first Lieutenant, and also when punishment is to be administered. All hands are always called to witness any punishment. After this painful operation is over, all hands go to breakfast, and at 9 o'clock the decks are again cleared for quarters. At that time, the drum and fife give notice that each one must be at his station. Some particular division is then ordered to exercise at the great guns; the drum and fife then play the retreat and the other divisions disperse; about once a week or two, general quarters take place, when all the guns are exercised at once, and all the evolutions are performed that are used upon a ship's going into action. Boarders are called to board, and then to repel boarders. The pikemen really stick at nothing over the waist of the ship, and cutlasses are used alarmingly; and the imaginary enemies are driven away, and all return to their stations. After performing other feats of valor, the guns are secured, the pikes, cutlasses, etc. are put in their places and thus ends a general quarters on board a man-of-war.

"At 10, the carpenters are at work on the larboard side of the gundeck, and the armorer in the waist. In fact, all are doing something. The watch below are mending clothes, making hats, etc., while the marines are scouring up the small arms to give them a good appearance at the cabin door. In this manner, the forenoon passes off. The idlers are reading, and the gundeck is quite a library. At 12 midday, an observation is taken by the master and midshipmen. The latitude is reported to the Captain, and the ship's company then get their dinner. The master, having ascertained the longitude by chronometer, marks the course upon the chart. At one the decks are again cleared up. At two and three o'clock, the officers dine and the afternoon passes off with reading, working, etc., until four o'clock. At six, the crew are inspected at quarters and the work for the day may be said to be completed.

"In the evening, the officers write, read, and play chess and backgammon, while the sailors are spinning long yarns, dancing, singing, etc. Time in this way at sea passes off quickly, and the monotony of the 'doldrums' or calms is enlivened by the capture of a shark or a dolphin. Sunday, however, is one of the most interesting days at sea. All work is suspended, and the decks have an extra scrub and the brass railings an extra polish. If it happens to be the first of the month, the 'articles of war' are read by the Captain in a clear and impressive manner, while the sailors surround the capstan. Afterwards, divine service is performed, the crew mustered and the day passes off quietly, a day of rest." Sick report has 33 men. Latitude 8.06 south/Longitude 47.27 east.]

[On December 18, 1844, Captain's Clerk B.F. Stevens added a description of the crew:

"Within a few days past the officers in the different divisions have been engaged in finding out as near as possible the proportion the foreigners bear on board ship to the native born Americans and the result is as follows: 200 Americans, 8 Canadians, 1 West Indian, 35 English, 34 Irish, 12 Scotch, 6 French, 16 German, 11 Dutch, 4 Hamburg, 1 Bremen, 2 Prussians, 4 Russians, 3 Norwegians, 14 Swedes, 6 Danes, 5 Welsh, 1 Mahonese, 2 Portugal, 2 Italian, 1 Australian, 1 Peruvian, 1 Swiss, 5 Chinese; making 175 foreigners. The result does not include the officers or marines. Allowing 32 officers and 20 marines, for Americans, and 20 marines for foreigners, the result would be 252 Americans, 195 foreigners, being ten less than the actual number of persons onboard.

"We now have been 120 days within the tropics, and over 60 upon the African and Madagascar coasts, and during this time have not lost a man. The greatest number upon the sick list has been 43, and no dangerous cases. Fevers and diarrhoea predominate, but are the effects of imprudence, such as sleeping upon wet decks, eating large quantities of fruit, partly unripe. I do not think another case could be found where a ship of the size of the Constitution, with 457 souls onboard, has cruised so long in such climates, with the above happy result. There is certainly no village in the most healthy parts of the world containing the same number of individuals as this ship, where death has not occurred in the space of seven months."]

[Thomas journal continues:]

December 20, 1844 -- Since leaving Rio, the ship has been painted white or lead color with a red streak, in place of black with a white streak. The idea was originated by Captain Percival, and everyone onboard can bear testimony to its success; the ship is cooler, both inside and out, and a degree of comfort pervades the gun and berth decks, very acceptable to the sick. During the hottest days, the thermometer being upwards of 100 degrees in the sun, it is almost impossible to bear one's hand upon the black hammock clothes, while the side of the ship is perfectly cool. Again in the hottest weather when in a ship painted black, the pitch will be issuing from the seams in the bends, we are troubled by no such complaint.

It has always been a favorite idea, theoretically, that white would reflect the rays of the sun to a greater degree than a black or darker color; practically, it has been proven so in the case of this ship, and Captain Percival deserves the praise of all concerned in real improvements for successfully introducing the above plan. It is noted by our scientist that Dr. Benjamin Franklin had already experimented with such ideas as well as peasant farmers in Switzerland as they would place various tinted clothes across freshly sewn fields to induce various climate controls, but it remained up to the Constitution to prove this theory correct with fighting ships.

At 5:30, all hands were called to quarters for inspection. At 7 a.m., the sad news of the sudden death of John Weston, seaman, was reported. He had been our first death and the crew almost expected at this point to be spared from the vengeful wreckage of life that death creates. He had been sick for four days and then made a recovery, leaving many behind that were much sicker than he. He was found on the berth deck, not too far from the sick bay. Several men who found him that he was moaning, but no one recorded his last words. The surgeon thought that fever might have been the cause of death. But upon cutting the body, and further inspecting the corpse, Weston was found to have badly decayed lungs. All hands were called to bury the dead and the solemn occasion has saddened the entire crew. The ceremony of reading the burial service was performed by Lieutenant Paine. The body of seaman John P. Weston was taken to the gangway and committed to the deep. An American Jack was placed upon it. The splash of the body into the sea broke many of the crew into tears and it is best not to elaborate further on this matter. Distance made these 24 hours is 100 miles. Sick list has 44 men. Latitude 1.30 south/longitude 77.27 east.

December 22, 1844 -- At 9:30, the crew was inspected at quarters. At 10:00, a Divine Service was read by Captain Percival. We have had another death onboard ship. This time the deceased is Christian Fisher. He was a German by birth and was said to have a great amount of musical talent, as his position onboard was that of a bandsman.

His body was given up to the sea that evening as his son watched. Many of the crew remarked how well the boy behaved during the entire ordeal and that his loyalty to his father was unflinching. Because of the many who are sick aboard ship, Captain

Percival has ordered the forward cabin converted immediately into a hospital. Four of the more serious sick have already been removed to the improvised quarters. The sick list has 46 men. Distance made these 24 hours is 147 miles. Latitude 1.15 south/Longitude 80.24 east.

December 24, 1844 -- We have tried to sell the last belongings and clothing of our deceased seamen, J.P. Weston and Christian Fisher. Our colors are still at half-mast and the sick list continues to grow. Some onboard think that the myth about the Sultan's water being contaminated has caused quite a stir about the men, but so far, all the deaths have been from other causes as the post mortems have proven. Still, there seems to be a darker cloud gathering with us than before when all seemed so bright for the whole crew. The sick report for our Christmas Eve now carries 54 men who suffer such agonies. Distance made these 24 hours is 75 miles. Latitude 0.23 south/Longitude 85.05 east.

December 25, 1844 -- There have been some special liberties extended to the men and prayers and quiet thoughts turned toward home and Gosport this special day. The carpentry shop has made a goodly assortment of ornaments to rig below. Captain Percival has given permission for a grog to be served the men with extra rations for the crew. The joy and thoughts towards Virginia that this day was certain to bring are now overshadowed by a growing number of our sick. So we have passed our Christmas day at sea. It has been two days since the forward cabin has been made into a hospital for their growing number. Cots were hung up and four men brought in. They are here more comfortable and less crowded than in the sick bay or gun deck. Captain Percival has shown great feelings towards the sick and he has a real desire to see that they are as comfortable as possible. On board ship, the sick are very frequently excluded from receiving any more attention than necessary for the various illnesses, particularly when the list is large. There, the acts by the Captain for their personal comfort are a credit to the navy and should be acknowledged.

December 30, 1844 -- Commenced with light and pleasant weather. At 5:30, the crew was inspected at quarters. The middle part was pleasant with light air and some calms. At 9:30, it was reported to the Captain that John Peters, seaman, departed this life. An examination took place. Distance made these 24 hours is 38 miles. Sick list has 61 men. Latitude 2.58 north/Longitude 92.25 east.

January 1, 1845 -- The sailmakers are busily employed making a new fore topsail. At 4, we bent the larboard cable and got the larboard anchor off the bow. At 9:20, we burned a blue light to a sail to our leeward carrying a light. At 3 a.m., we tacked

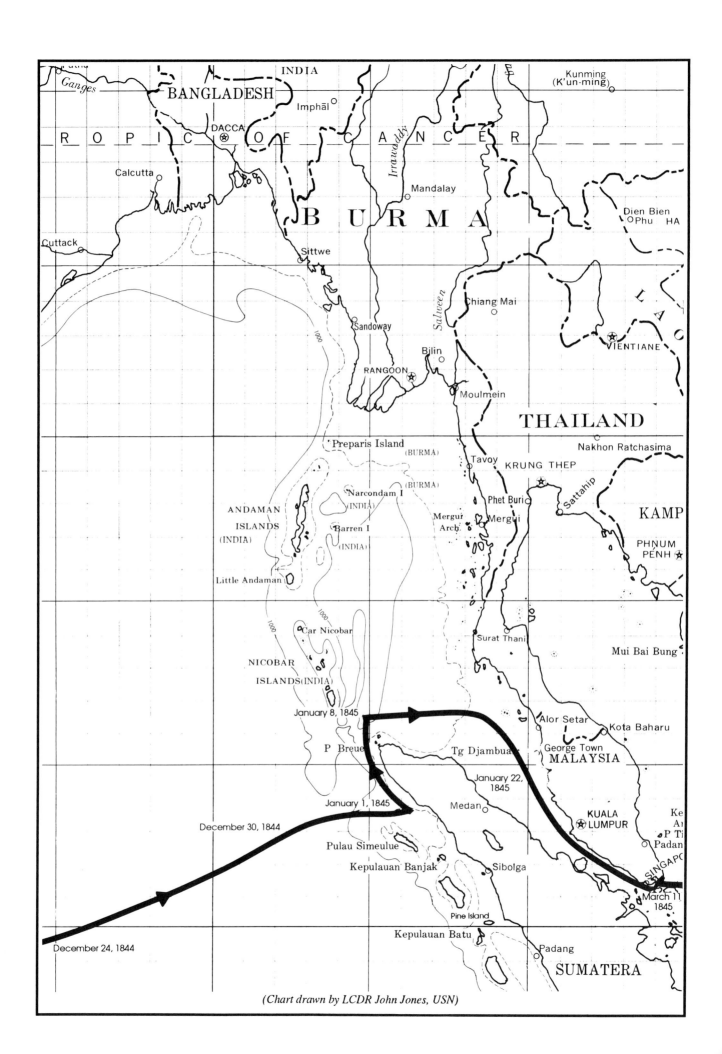

(Chart drawn by LCDR John Jones, USN)

ship to the north. At daylight we could make land on the weather beam. Many were certain the land to be Sumatra. At 9 a.m., the crew was inspected at quarters. Land in sight on the lee bow. The ship is under royals and flying jib. Latitude 3.27 north/Longitude 95.59 east.

January 2, 1845 -- At 5, casted the lead with 40 fathom line. We found no bottom. At 6, the appearance of land was certain on the leeward and on the weather bow. At 7, almost the entire crew was called to witness the flight of the most beautiful comet. At 8, got a cast of lead with 40 fathoms and still found no certain bottom. During the 4th watch, sounded every half hour with a 50 fathom line and this time found the bottom to be from muddy to sandy. At 1 a.m., we came to with the kedge in 50 fathoms water. Furled sail. Sick report lists 66 men. Latitude 3.40 north/Longitude 96.14 east.

Off Sumatra Island

January 3, 1845 -- At 1, hove up the kedge and got underway. We made all the sails before the wind as we stood in for Sumatra [the most western island in present day Indonesia]. At 4:30, we took in all the steering sail and tried to run down a proa [a native boat of Sumatra, often used by pirates]. We hoisted the white flag as is the custom of the sea, that is to show them that we were friendly. They paid us no attention, but rather took an evasive course.

In Pursuit of Pirates off Sumatra

January 3, 1845 -- We then fired a blank cartridge from the carronade no. 21. The proa still paid no attention to our signal to come alongside. At 5:30, after giving sufficient time and warning, we loaded shot and fired a gun just ahead of the proa. This time she hove to and took in all sail. We then ran her down, backing our topsail.

A boat was lowered and sent alongside the pirate. As our men clearly showed their cutlass and pistol, the proa made no attempt to struggle even though there were loud protests from them. The boat returned with the head of the louts and what appeared to be stolen articles of silver and gold that had no business on a proa. Articles of clothing from several nationalities including the American navy were also turned over to us. They all seemed frightened beyond their wits after their capture but were taken below under the heaviest guard. Sumatra at this time was at a distance of 10 miles.

After their capture, we sounded in 20 fathoms of water and found a muddy bottom. We took the proa in tow and filled away. At 5:30, Cape Felix bore compass Southeast by East 1/2 East. [Cape Felix, Qullah Batto, Cocoam Point, and Wylah which follow in the Thomas journal are all extinct names that served as trading centers and landfalls for the Constitution's survey and patrol against pirates in the area of what is probably today the islands of Batu and Pini which are located just off shore on the west, central side of Sumatra.] We stood along the coast of Sumatra with lights clearly seen along the coast. At 10:30, we shortened sail and came to with the kedge in 21 fathoms of water. Furled the sails. During the night we experienced a very heavy dew.

At 6:30, got underway with a light breeze from the north and stood down the coast. Our destination was the coast and the Harbor of Soosoo. Cape Felix bore compass East by North. At 9:30, we discovered a ship at anchor in Quallah Battoo Bay. At 11:30, we reduced sail to topsail and jib. At the meridian we were standing in for the anchorage at Quallah Battoo. Sick report has 63 men.

Sumatra
Quallah Battoo

January 4, 1845 -- At 1, the sails were shortened and at 2, the ship came to with the kedge in 22 fathoms of water. Veered to by the 50 fathom hawser and furled sails. Took the following bearing of the town Quallah Battoo-bearing North, Cocoam Point East 3/4 North. The Captain of the American Ship Caroline Augusta of Salem, Massachusetts is in company.

The well known Po Adam came to visit our ship. He was a Malay native whose bravery had saved the lives of the Captain and crew of the Friendship. A description of him can be found in other articles, including any on voyages of the Potomac. His appearance is not very inspiring and though America owes him for his brave deed, he is pure Malay and can not be fully trusted. We have discharged the pirates, who we forced to serve as pilots for the harbor. They have been taken under guard to the right authority on shore.

The drought [draft] of the ship was taken today and measures 22 feet, 9 inches aft, and 20 feet, 10 inches forward. With each wind, a most delightful perfume from the spice trees scents the air. At 10:00 a.m., we sent a boat ashore and brought back the Rajah to visit the ship.

[Ship's Clerk Stevens witnessed the meeting when the Rajah of the Town of Quallah Battoo with his tagrag [sic] bobtail, called on the Captain:

"Quite a party congregated in the cabin. The Captain then explained to the Malays the object of his visit to the coast of Sumatra. He gave them to understand that America had a good many big ships to protect their commerce from the attacks of pirates. After much talk, the chiefs said they wished for peace and to trade with the Americans. No dependance can be placed on their word. Our commerce in this part of the world, which is always increasing, requires the protection of our ships of war, particularly on this coast, where the Malays will massacre the crews and cut off the vessels. I did not go ashore at Quallah Battoo, in consequence of my health, which had been suffering a few days previous to our arrival from an attack of diarrhoea. The Captain has also been severely ill with the gout in his feet and right hand, and my presence was necessary on board."]

January 5, 1845 -- While laying here, positive orders were given by the Captain against any man being allowed to eat fruit and an order was given to prevent any boat with fruit in it from coming alongside the ship. Many men were disgruntled at the lack of freedom to purchase the fruit they desired, however, the native boats ladened with pineapples and other fruits were pushed off and warned of the restriction. What would have been the consequence had we not taken this precautionary measure? The entire crew would be dead, that's what. Sick report has 64 men.

January 6, 1845 -- Po Adam came onboard as our pilot. In consequence of the Potomac Affair he has been robbed of his money which amounted to $20,000, his fort destroyed, and his position as a Rajah was taken from him. He was given the position of pilot more out of a consideration of charity than his talents for that duty. Many people in America have profited from his work and bravery for this country, but they have long forgotten him.

[The death notice and burial of Midshipman Lucius Mason follows:]

At 9:30, Midshipman Lucius M. Mason of Virginia departed this life after an illness of 12 days. He had dysentery and then an inflammation of the brain. The colours were set at half-mast.

During the time of his sickness his messmates watched with him, and exerted themselves with a zeal worthy of them. In the afternoon at 4 o'clock, Midshipman Mason was buried with the appropriate ceremonies due to an officer of his rank. The body was borne from the quarter deck to the gangway by four petty officers and two seaman who had attended him during his illness. His messmates followed the corpse, while the other officers stood uncovered as they passed. The band played a dead march, the colors were half-masted, and the occasion was indeed a solemn one. The coat, sword, and cap of the deceased were placed upon the body, the burial service was read and the body of our deceased friend was committed to the deep. The awful splash was heard, and the shock went to the heart of everyone. The guard then fired two volleys, and the crew dispersed, to think over the affair, as I trust many did, with thoughts directed heavenward.

Cape Felix bore compass Northwest 1/4 North at a distance of 9 miles. Sick report lists 65 men.

Off Wylah, Sumatra Island

January 8, 1845 -- We can see a barque and brig flying English colors. There are several small sails in sight to the leeward. Sumatra is to the north and east. We are sounding in from 25 to 13 fathoms of water. At 4, the ship was tacked. L.H. Peck was punished with 6 lashes of the colt for disobeying the Captain of the Afterguard [a seaman whose station was on the poop or quarterdeck to work the after gear of the ship].

At 5:30, the crew was inspected at quarters. At 8, most of the crew reported seeing a very bright comet to the south and west. At 9:30, the sails were furled and the ship came to by the kedge in 16 1/2 fathoms of water. We found a soft muddy bottom. We veered to the 40 fathoms hawser. Middle part of the day was pleasant as we made land on the larboard beam. At 5:30, the kedge was hoved up and the ship got underway again under plain sail. We discovered a vessel close in shore under sail and another at anchor. We are standing in for shore.

We are beating in for an anchorage off Wylah. At 10:30, came to with the kedge. We were in 12 fathoms of water with a muddy bottom. Took the following bearings on compass viz. Town of Wylah bearing North Northeast 3/4 East at a distance of 5 miles. Qually Hill bore Northwest 1/2 North. We found the American Ship Rome under Captain Brown and the Caroline Augusta both of Salem. The ships in this area are engaged in the pepper trade, the Rome being the first American merchant vessel to have ever landed here and the Constitution, the first national vessel that ever put in here.

At Sea

The sailmakers have finished the new fore topsail. At 6:30, we can plainly see the southern point of Grand Nicobar Island [the southern part of a chain of islands now called the Andaman and Nicobar Islands which run from the southern tip of Burma to the most northern extreme of Sumatra]. Its compass bearing was West South West. At 5:30, the crew was inspected at quarters. Single-reefed the topsail and brought down the mizzen-royal yard. At sunset the above island bore compass West by South. During the night we have had squally weather. We have made and reduced sail as conditions permitted and required. Our next destination of Singapore could prove difficult to reach as the winds through the [Malacca] straits [runs between Sumatra and Malaysia] are very unpredictable.

During the morning watch the weather became particularly troublesome and we furled the mainsail, reefed and set the spanker and bent the fore and main trysails. The latter part of the day was moderate so that we lowered spanker and unbent foresail. At 11, set the spanker, and foresail. Sick report has 56 men. Latitude 6.26 north/Longitude 94.52 east.

January 22, 1845 -- At 4 p.m., we could make Palo Penang [major Malaysian port on the northwest side of the peninsula, near the present border of Thailand] which bore East 1/2 North. We also have a sail in sight on the weather beam. At 8 p.m., we sounded in 34 1/2 fathoms of water; the bottom was a blue mud. During the night we experienced light breezes and occasional calms. Sounded in from 28 to 31 fathoms of water. At daylight we discovered a sail on the lee and one on the weather bow. Palo Penang is in sight on the weather quarter. Land ahead. At 9, the crew was inspected at quarters. At 10 a.m., we unbent the foresail and bent another. We are standing down the Straits of Malacca shore. Sick report has 57 men. Latitude 4.51 north/Longitude 100.30 east.

January 30, 1845 -- At 8:30, the crew was inspected at quarters. We took the following compass bearings: Out Water Island, Northwest 1/4 North, Moura Mountain East Northeast 1/4 East, Formosa Mountain East 1/4 South. We reduced sail because of a squall accompanied by heavy rain. Sounding in from 23 to 20 fathoms of water. We hope to reach Singapore shortly, perhaps by the first of February. At 9 p.m., Peter Wolf, Captain of the main hold departed this life. His body was in the forward cabin hospital and the surgeon determined he died of dysentery after being ill for two months.

At 9 a.m., all hands were called to bury the dead. The flag was half-masted. The Captain read the burial service and the remains of Peter Wolf were committed to the deep. At meridian, Palo Penang bore east by south.

Singapore Straits

February 2, 1845 -- At 7 p.m., we weighed the kedge and made all plain sail. At 12:30, set the starboard studding sails. We showed our colors to an English barque standing to the north. We stood in for Rabbit Island. At 5:40, we shortened our sail and came to with the kedge. We veered to with the hawser and furled the sail.

Took the following compass bearing viz. the south point of Barn Island East by North. Tree Island was Southwest by West. At 5:30, we called all hands and got underway with all plain sail. We are standing in for Singapore [British trading colony at the southern end of the Malay peninsula].

At 8, had the ship pumped. At 11:30, the sails were clewed up and came to with the larboard anchor in 10 fathoms of water with a muddy bottom. Veered to with the 13 fathom chain and furled the sails.

An officer from the H.B.W. Frigate Cambrian bearing the broad pennant of Commodore Chads of the Royal Navy came over to greet us. We could also see several steamers of the Royal Navy and the H.B.W. Brig Wolverine. We took the next compass bearing by using the flagstaff in the town of Singapore; Northwest 3/4 West. The flagstaff on Signal Hill was Southwest by West. Signal Island was South by West. Sick report has 58 men.

Singapore

February 3, 1845 -- At 2 p.m., with the English Flag in the fore, we saluted the town with 21 guns. Our salute was returned gun for gun from shore. At 3 p.m., the topsails were loosened and we saluted the broad pennant of Commodore Chads of the English squadron with 15 guns, which was returned by the H.B.W. Frigate Cambrian gun for gun.

We then furled the sails again. The American Consul, Mr. Balestier, was received for a visit. He graciously offered Captain Percival his home for temporary quarters while the Constitution was in port.

At 5 p.m., the Frigate Cambrian half-masted colors in our honor and we replied by half-masting ours. We were all pleased to take on new and fresh supplies; fresh beef, bread, and vegetables were brought for the crew. Thank God that we also received a tank of fresh water to replace our old. Perhaps there will be fewer sicknesses.

At 11:00 a.m., the English Commodore Chads visited our ship. He was the first Lieutenant of the Java when she was captured by this ship, and because of the death of Captain Lambert, he was obliged to surrender her [refers to the famous battle off South America during the War of 1812 between the Constitution under Captain Bainbridge and H.M.S. Java under Captain Lambert.]

Sick report has 60 men.

February 5, 1845 -- Everyone busily employed in re-stocking general ship supplies and fresh water. Already, we have replaced 1100 gallons of water in the tanks. While at anchor in the harbor of Singapore we have had two men passed from amongst us. They are Charles Springer and Stephen Hoyt; they are to be buried on shore.

February 24, 1845 -- Several of the crew are on liberty from the ship.

[The following report is made by Ship's Clerk B.F. Stevens on their visit to Singapore:

"I am pleased to visit a place of such importance. The number of Chinese is about 60,000 exclusive of the floating population. There are but about 300 English, while the remainder of the inhabitants are composed of Malays and people from different parts of Asia.

"It is said that from eight to ten thousand people arrive in Singapore monthly, mostly Chinese. The streets in Singapore are arranged in the English plan, and are extremely neat. I mean those apart from the business part of the city where the English reside. The bazaars of the Chinese are kept clean and in good order, and the variety of fancy articles to be met with therein are astonishing. There are two hotels here, both of which appear to be excellent houses. Thus far I am well pleased with my view of Singapore.

"Having had an excellent opportunity of seeing Singapore, I shall give my ideas upon it without fear or trembling. A few days after our arrival the Captain had not recovered from an attack of the gout, took up residence on shore with the American Consul Mr. Balestier. Mrs. Balestier, an extremely courteous and hospitable woman, was found to be a real Yankee spirit. She is the daughter of Paul Revere, of Boston, whose memory is cherished by his countrymen. Mr. Balestier's mansion and plantation are about three miles from the business part of the city. To reach them we pass through excellent roads, beautifully laid out and ornamented by shrubbery of various kinds. Around this mansion the consul has planted a hedgerow [sic] of pineapples. This may seem strange, but it is nevertheless true. The most beautiful fruit of this description can be had for one cent each.

"Here, too, we obtained the delicious mangosteen [mango fruit] so highly extolled by all East India travelers. The fruit is shaped like an orange and is about as large.

The inside resembles a kind of jelly or grape and dissolves in the mouth. It seems that enough can not be had.

"I had the opportunity of seeing a Malay juggler, who performs his feats adroitly, one of the most astonishing was swallowing a sword. He did this without any trouble. This feat, though very disgusting to me, was an interesting one. I had heard so much praise of the Malay juggling that I could have witnessed anything in the shape of a trick. The other feats, such as hiding balls, etc., were performed upon bare ground, and were more cleverly done than any I have ever witnessed. The performer begged for a shilling, which I gave him, and thought myself not over generous.

"Another treat to me was a visit to the opium shops. The time which I went was not a favorable one, being in the afternoon, but I saw enough to give me a good idea of an opium smoker. The interior of the shop is very plain. On a long counter lay several Chinese, with each a pipe and a lamp, who, upon our entering, had hardly enough strength to raise their heads. It seems as if the fumes of the drugs were fast stupefying them,--all their thoughts appeared to be upon pleasure they were deriving, and they would occasionally greet us with a smile, the most idiotic you can imagine. I left disgusted with my visit, though I had certainly obtained some information about.

"I had the pleasure of seeing an orang-outang at the London Hotel. It certainly had the appearance, in the face, of an extremely ugly person, but not in form. This specimen was from Borneo- was six months old and about three feet high. Its crying resembled that of a child, though much louder and harsher. It was truly pitiful to hear its moans when a pineapple was taken from it. It rolled over and over, tore its hair, bit the chain, etc., and anger was truly portrayed. I never expect, nor do I wish to see an animal so near the human race, in appearance, again.

"At the burial service of Springer and Hoyt, we had followed the bodies to the graveyard atop the city. The view is most spectacular, as the city stretches mile after mile; the peculiar houses of the English residents and the Malay huts, with nicely thatched roofs- together with coconut trees, form the most beautiful picture, equal to anything that I have ever seen.

"After leaving the graveyard, I stopped to gather a few nutmegs from the trees, so as to carry with me to America an evidence of my observation.

"It is a strange circumstance that within two miles of Singapore is an island so sickly that it with difficulty even Malays can be found to attend upon the signals. The marshes are said to produce sickness. Our naturalist, Dr. Reinhardt, visited it and examined carefully into the causes, of which the above is the principal one. [This is

one of the first links of marshland with the causes of Malaria. Dr. Walter Reed
identified a variety of swamp mosquita in Cuba after the Spanish-American War of
1898 as the carrier.]

"Singapore is said to be the healthy port of India, and one
reason of it is that the lower classes bathe so frequently. On ascending the river,
plenty of men, women, and children, who live on boats on each side, are seen
performing their ablutions.

"The 22nd. of February being the anniversary of Washington's birthday, a salute
was fired at meridian, and in the evening, as usual on such occasions, rockets were
sent off, and blue light burned. The old ship looked beautiful, and her appearance
attracted a crowd of spectators on shore, drawn thither by the novelty of the scene."]

[Thomas journal continues:]

February 25, 1845 -- We received on board 13,300 lbs. of ship bread. We also
received a good quantity of firewood. The main and fore yards were lifted. New
slings were fitted to the main yard. At 10:30, the sail was lessened. The boatswain
and his mates are employed overhauling and examining the rigging.

February 27, 1845 -- At 1, the H.B.M. Sloop of War Wolf came in and anchored.
It was last from Hong Kong. We sent a party over to visit her and obtain information.
We received from the tank alongside 4,306 gallons of water. At 2 p.m., we furled the
sail. Received various stores onboard in the carpenters department. Unbent the
mizzen topsail and sent it down for repairs. The Sloop of War Wolf went to sea. The
American Ship Chio of Boston and 4 months from home and the Batavia came in and
anchored. We are busily employed in staging the mast and setting up the rigging.
Sent more of the crew on liberty. Sick report has 28 men.

March 1, 1845 -- At 11 a.m., the Commander-in-Chief of the Cochin China
Squadron, 3 ships, visited us with his suite. [This is one of the earliest records of
American military interest in Cochin China or Vietnam.]

March 8, 1845 -- James Corbit, seaman, and an Irishman, has been discharged
because of misconduct. We are taking on more fresh water from a tank alongside.
The 2nd. cutter is loading sand onboard and the 4th. cutter is engaged in assisting the
towing of the Dutch War Steamer Merapi closer into the town. The Commander of
the Dutch Steamer Merapi is visiting the ship. We are all employed in making
preparations to go to sea.

The following men have not returned from liberty: Michael Jennings, John Williams, and George Anderson. John Robinson, an Englishman and Peter Hennessy, an Irishman, have been discharged.

Ship's drought-aft, 22 feet 10 inches, forward, 21 feet 3 inches.

Chapter Three

The South China Sea and Pacific Ocean Voyages

At Sea

March 11, 1845 -- At 4:15. got underway and stood out to sea by the wind. We are under plain sail. At 5 p.m., shot all the guns one round shot. At 6 p.m., we could see Bingtang Island [present day Bintan island is located at the eastern extreme of the Malacca Straits as it empties into the South China Sea just south of Singapore], north point on a compass bearing of Southeast by East 1/2, distance 5 miles.

There is a sail in sight. At 10:30 p.m., we anchored with the kedge in 22 fathoms of water. At daylight, we called all hands and brought the kedge up and made plain sail on the larboard tack. At 8, Point Romani [Point Romani and the John Hill which follows are landfalls on Bintan Island] bore North by East 1/2 East. John Hill bore Northwest by West. Bintang Hill bore Southeast 1/2 East. There are several sails in sight. At 9 a.m., the crew was inspected at quarters. The 2nd. division exercised their guns. Sick report has 31 men. Latitude 1.12.30 north/Longitude 104.48 east.

March 13, 1845 -- At 1:30, squalls to the windward began to pick up. During these 24 hours we made and reduced sails as situation required. The sailmakers and the gang are busily employed making a new main topsail. At 3:30, the crew was inspected at quarters. At 7:30, the ship was tacked, the foresail was unbent for repairs and another was bent. At 8 a.m., we sounded in 32 fathoms of water. We found a mud bottom. At 9 a.m., we exercised at general quarters. At 9:40, the ship was tacked again. At 10:20, a new tack was made. The Boatswain was employed in overhauling and repairing the rigging. Our destination is Borneo City [now called Brunei, the capital of Sarawak, independent from Borneo proper]. Latitude 1.23 north/Longitude 106.13 east.

March 15, 1845 -- At 2 p.m., we sighted land on the weather bow. At 4 p.m., Julian Island is insight bearing south southeast. At 5 p.m., the ship was tacked. At 5:30 p.m., went to quarters as usual. At sunset, another island was insight. This time it was on the lee quarter and bore South by East 1/4 East.

Another island on the weather quarter was supposed to be Campbell Island and bore Northeast 3/4 East. At 9, the ship was tacked, and at midnight the ship was tacked again. At 2 a.m., the ship was tacked once more, and as daylight appeared, we made the small islands called the Saddles [part of greater Tambelan Island, Borneo] on the weather bow. Campbell and St. Julian are on the lee bow. The 5th. division was exercised. We made and reduced sail as situation required. We should reach the mouth of the Sambas River soon. Latitude 1.19 north/Longitude 107.00 east.

March 19, 1845 -- We are now off the coast of Borneo and at the mouth of the Sambas River. The river is a major avenue of exploration into this forbidden and inhospitable land. The Constitution is the first American warship to have ever visited here and every precaution is being taken to defend the ship and the exploration party preparing to leave the ship.

The Master is in the 4th. cutter just lowered. Their orders are to examine the coast in the vicinity of the Sambas River [runs into the South China Sea from the extreme eastern tip of Borneo, just below Sarawac]. At 1:30, we got underway again and discovered the mouth of the river. We anchored in 7 1/2 fathoms of water with the larboard anchor and veered to with the 25 fathoms chain. The entrance of the river bore southeast by east at a distance of 5 miles. There is a northern point of land in sight bearing North Northeast 1/2 East. The southern point bore Southwest by West 1/4 West.

March 19, 1845 -- We furled the sails. At 4, the master returned onboard ship. We then hoisted out our first cutter and unbent the fore topsail for repairs. The 1st. cutter and gig formed the next expedition under the command of Lieutenant William C. Chaplin.

The following officers were also under his command: Lt. of Marines J.W. Curtis, Acting Master Strain, Midshipman Colville Tenett, Assistant Surgeon M. Duvall, and Naturalist J.C. Reinhardt. The company was also made up of 23 seamen and 3 marines.

They were to go up the river to a Dutch settlement by the same name of Sambas under the orders of Captain Percival to reconnoiter the entire area. As the natives of Borneo are well known for their treacherous savagery, the mission was compelled to arm themselves in case they should be attacked. The jib was unbent for repairs as the crew is variously employed. Sick report lists 27 men.

March 20, 1845 -- The Chinese junk that we saw at a distance yesterday has gone up the river. A Malay pirate vessel has also gone up the river. There is a great deal of discomfort aboard concerning the safety of the expedition. The temperature in the shade now stands at 84 degrees.

March 21, 1845 -- Our sailmakers are employed in repairing the jib and spanker. We have learned that the boats sent up the river on the 19th., under the Command of Lieutenant Strain are making the best of their way down toward the ship. To protect them further, we armed and sent the 3rd. cutter up the Sambas River to the Chinese town under the charge of Lieutenant J.W. Cooke. The following officers accompanied him: Lieut. J.B. Dale, Surgeon McLeod, Professor of Mathematics E. Eastabrook and Midshipman J.J. Cooke.

At 9 p.m., all the boats returned safely. All were well and very pleased with the expedition. The country is represented as very beautiful and they found no fault with the hospitalities [sic] they received from the natives and settlers in the town of Sambas. The Chinese town was also considered friendly. On the arrival of the officers in Sambas, the officers and crew were kindly received and had apartments furnished them by the Governor who appears to be a fine old Dutch gentleman.

March 22, 1845 -- At daylight, we hoisted the 1st. cutter. At 6:30, all hands were called to get up the anchor and we got underway, made sail, and stood along the coast of Borneo.

[The following report was made by Midshipman Colville Tenett on the expedition and entered into this journal this day:

"March 19th., at 9:30, the expedition got underway with Lieutenant Chaplin in command. We left the ship and pulled on for the Sambas River. At 11:15, we entered the river and found two guard pirate vessels at anchor. We boarded one (no.

3) and endeavored to obtain a pilot. We were refused. We did obtain information respecting the course of the river.

"A few minutes after leaving the pirate vessel, they dispatched a boat, which at first took us by surprise. This boat went up ahead and acted as a guide up the river. The stretch up the river is about two miles.

"March 20th., at 3:00 p.m., we saw a large pirate vessel under sail moving down the river. Finally, we took our guide boat alongside and lashed the two together and sailed as one. The second stretch was 12 miles bearing East 1/2, North 1/4, a mile wide. We are sounding from 1 and 1/2 to 4 fathoms.

"The third stretch was 8 miles bearing Northeast 1/2 East. At 2 p.m., we passed a pirate vessel fully manned but apparently unarmed. At 3, we found ourselves in a heavy lightning and thunder storm. The fourth stretch bore north for 8 miles. At 6 p.m., we entered a small branch of the river and recruited the other boats crew. At 8, we anchored in the main stream in 3 fathoms. At 9, we weighed anchor and made sail again. At midnight, we entered the right branch.

"Just previous to getting underway, a Malay boat came alongside and made enquiries regarding the expedition. We gave our answers as judiciously as possible. We found slack water at midnight and passed a Chinese junk. At 5:10, we arrived off the town of Sambas. "Anchored at daylight, Lieutenant Chaplin called on the Dutch Governor. At 6 a.m., we landed the men. The temperature of the air was around 94 degrees. Through the kindness of the Governor, we obtained a shelter for our men.

"March 21 was very rainy, air at 86 degrees. At 7 p.m., we left Sambas and sailed down the river on our return to the ship. We passed several boats in the river. At midnight, we re-entered the main stream and then ran aground again. After some delay on the left side of the river, got off uninjured. At 2 a.m., we caught the flood tide and finally made it back to the ship".]

[Ship's Clerk B.F. Stevens reported on the expedition as well:

". . . Mr. Baumgardt, the Governor of Sambas, received the expedition very kindly and gave every information in his power to the officer in command.

"He states that the country for miles around is one great marsh. The tide usually overflows the marsh and low lands. The Chinese are the traders in the place, and that all the cotton fabrics, etc., come through them. That about 25,000 dollars of washed gold dust is taken annually from the Sambas, and that a kind of wood called Izer is brought from the interior and taken to China and then made into fancy works. The wood is extremely hard, and it is supposed to last one hundred years.

"The fort in the town is made of it, and has been standing for thirty years, and no rot has appeared. It is a singular fact that no white man has ever seen this kind of wood growing. It is brought from the Diaks [a major native tribe on Borneo] to the Chinese, and by them sold to traders. Nothing of the interior is known, no European having penetrated more than sixty or seventy miles from the coast.

"Mr. Baumgardt supposes from the immense quantities of gold in possession of the natives, that it abounds in every part of the island in great abundance.

"We have had a small trade with the Sambas, but it is now ceased, being wholly in the hands of the Dutch. The Governor appeared desirous of having it again. He said that a demand for our cottons would arise. The only two articles that are excluded are salt and gunpowder which are monopolized by the Government. The only tax is one rupee [about 40 cents then] per ton, on foreign vessels, and a half on Dutch vessels. No danger need be apprehended at Sambas from the natives, who are completely under the control of the Dutch, though at many places on the coast, particularly at Borneo proper, the Malays are extremely treacherous, and have massacred several parties of traders.

"Much valuable information was obtained by Captain Percival, by which the Government will have knowledge hereafter of those regions, as the Constitution is believed to be the first American man-of-war that has ever visited Borneo.

"I wish to also mention that Dr. Reinhardt, our naturalist, who accompanied the expedition, penetrated into the woods and discovered many flowers and plants, thus increasing his store of botanical knowledge.

"While the expedition was underway, the third cutter was sent ashore with a party of officers, who visited a Chinese town at the mouth of the Sambas River. It was similar to the part of Singapore occupied by the Chinese. They found our cottons there, and much preferred to the English. Gold dust is the only tender, and it is said to be worth $320.00 the pound. The officers returned much pleased with their visit."]

[Thomas journal continues:]

March 31, 1845 -- We made and reduced sail as occasion required. At sunset and 9 a.m., the crew was inspected. It was reported to the Captain that several of the marines and seamen had become cross with each other and several fights were reported. One of the more serious incidents of this nature was between marine Arthur Deblueg and seaman Thomas Starkey. Starkey being the principal instigator was given one dozen lashes of the cat, while the marine was given only nine lashes.

It was further reported to the men that these were some of the most dangerous waters that we would sail in since we had been followed since nearing Borneo by a large school of sharks. Unfortunate and tragic it would be for a man to fling another overboard in a fit of anger for that would surely be the end of him. Sick report has 19 men. Latitude 4.23 north/Longitude 112.17 east.

April 1, 1845--We made and reduced sail as the occasion called for necessary changes. As we have entered dangerous waters and reports from various ships are sufficient warning against possible incidents. We have begun exercising our marines in small arms fire at various targets. The cutters are also being exercised for exchanges with a possible enemy. Most of the drills concern themselves with defending the cutters in withdrawal or landings. Latitude 4.13 north/Longitude 112.07 east.

April 4, 1845 -- We are sounding every 24 hours in 40 fathoms water. The bottom appears to be soft, muddy water above extremely green. We have continued to pump the ship.

The 1st. and 3rd. cutters are being exercised in firing at various targets. Our marines are now practicing firing at targets while they are suspended from the fore yard arm to give cover to the cutters. Our gun divisions have also commenced practicing for cover and support as well. Latitude 4.10 north/Longitude 113.21 east.

Off Borneo

April 7, 1845 -- Upon entering the Borneo River [a tributary of what is now Brunei Bay, northwest Sarawak] we discovered a brig. A boat was sent over to board her and it proved to be the English Brig Ariel from Singapore and prepared to return with a cargo. The ship is under the larboard topmast and topgallant studding sails. We are standing in for the mouth of the Borneo River. Sounding in 13 fathoms of water, mostly a coral bottom. The water is very blue.

April 7, 1845 -- At 4:40, we clewed up and came to with the larboard anchor in 6 fathoms of water. We made a boat out front most of the time and take the soundings as often as needed. We then furled the sails and took the following bearing; Nio Isle bore West 1/4 North, the southern extremity of Great Roosoocan bore North by West 3/4. We sent a boat to board a brig that we spoke. She proved to be an English trading brig from Singapore.

We then sounded in toward the harbor of Borneo. It lays open to the north and west. We became between a Tree island and Great Roosoocan inlet. The harbor is very poorly charted and we spent some time in redrawing our charts. We steered for the high ground on each side of the bay. The bay itself is 80 miles in length from the mouth of the river.

Borneo

April 8, 1845 -- Got out the 1st, cutter and sent her up to the City of Borneo [now Brunei, capital of Sarawak]. The gig and the 3rd. cutter were sent along as escort in the expedition. We had reports that there was abundant coal in the area and we hoped that an agreement between the Sultan and our country could be reached concerning the mining of coal. Extra defenses were carried along since it has been reported to us that the Sultan controls the pirate activity around these waters.

At 1 p.m., we got the ship underway, and stood nearer into land. We anchored in 6 fathoms of water with a muddy bottom. The following bearing were taken; southeast point of Moarro Island bore Southwest 3/4 South.

April 9, 1845 -- The expedition proceeded up the river to the city of Borneo. They were kindly received by the Sultan. He saluted them upon their arrival with a salute of 9 guns. The land on both sides of the river is high and beautiful. The scenery is of a rich and picturesque kind. All the hills are covered by a verdure and the mountain breezes are loaded with perfumes. The river is about half a mile wide at the city. At every bend of the river there is a battery planted so as to sweep the boats ascending the city. These batteries are very well concealed by the high grass. The guns are mostly of brass. They are not mounted but rather lay on the ground and are sighted for one certain place along the river. The City of Borneo is one of the most singular in the world. It is built in the middle of the river. The streets are laid off in regular patterns and parallel to the shore. The main street is formed by the channel of the river. It is large and always filled with boats. It was singular to see everyone in boats, even children 4 or 5 years old in a canoe about the size of a bread tray. Some times they would capsize but even the young could swim like so many ducks. There is only one house on shore. The city contains 10 or 15,000 inhabitants. At the corner of every street there is a man stationed with a gong or chum to call all hands to arms. The Sultan protects pirates and now we have no doubt that he sends them out himself.

The inhabitants are Malays. The young ladies are very modest. Several of them ventured out to see the Americans as naked as the palm of a man's hand. It was enough to make one's mouth water. The natives are the Diaks. They are a dark and warlike tribe and known for their extreme savagery. Nothing is really known of them except for their extreme cruelty. They are at constant war with the inhabitants onshore.

April 9, 1845 -- The religion of the Malays is Mohometan. There government is completely despotic. The religion of the Diaks is still unknown. One of the few tribal customs to be generally known is that for a Diak warrior to have a wife, he must first have killed an enemy.

Near Borneo are extensive coal mines. The right to work them has been purchased by the English. Our mission to open this coal trade with America has therefore met with no success. Their principal export presently is said to be pepper. Ivory is also said to be an article of trade.

The island of Borneo is said to be the most extensive one in the world, except for New Holland. It has immense resources and is very fertile. It contains only three million inhabitants and is three or four times as extensive as Great Britain. There are very high mountains and long rivers on the isle.

Off Borneo

April 10, 1845 -- The Captain and Lieutenant Cook left the ship to visit the mouth of the Borneo River. We secured the boats for sea. Made preparations for going to sea. During the night, we observed much thunder and lightning over the land. At daylight, we got underway and stood towards the Laboan Isles. At 7:30, we sent the naturalist Dr. Reinhardt to examine the geological condition of the island. Dr. Reinhardt endeavored to ascertain as much as possible about the plants, etc. Hoved to and opened the spirit room to air. Latitude 5.47 north/Longitude 115.07 east.

April 11, 1845 -- Dispatched the 3rd. cutter to look out for the 4th. cutter. At 4 p.m., the cutters returned and were hoisted up. We made all plain sail on the wind. During the rest of the day we were employed trying to get clear of the numerous shoals not mentioned on the charts. There are many near and around Borneo. At 3, we finally shoaled, almost running aground. We came to by the employment of our kedge. Our small boats went out and sounded around the ship. During the remainder of the day, we felt our way out of the bay. Sick report lists 20 men. Distance made these 24 hours 29 miles. Latitude 5.47 north/Longitude 115.07 east.

April 13, 1845 -- The Constitution is in a very ticklish position as we are almost surrounded by shoals. None of them are marked on our charts. The entire crew now realizes that a shipwreck on such a wild and savage coast as Borneo could bring either death or slavery.

The ship is now under plain sail and standing to the south. We are slowly getting clear of one reef and running into another. At 10, all hands were called and the morning service was read. The ships company is now in fine spirits and fine health for this climate. Distance made these 24 hours 14 miles. Latitude 5.30 north/Longitude 115.05 east.

April 14, 1845 -- The ship is under plain sail. We are standing along the coast of Borneo. Tree Isle [not designated on available charts, however it is probably just south of Labuan Island on the northwest coast of Sarawak] is in sight and has a bearing of East by South 1/4 South. At 9, we anchored and soon got underway again. We are sounding during the day in 15 to 20 fathoms of water with a coral bottom. We have made the following scientific conclusion: The deep water has mostly a muddy bottom. Yet, from 20 to 2 fathoms of water, there is a coral bottom. Therefore, the difference can be told by the color of the water. The mud bottom has a sort of muddy green color, while the coral has a mixture of blue and green. Therefore, the difference can be told by the color of water. Distance made these 24 hours 27 miles. Latitude 5.07 north/Longitude 114.44 east.

April 17, 1845 -- We are sounding in 17 fathoms with a muddy bottom. We keep a boat ahead for sounding. At 4, the boat made signals of 15 fathoms. We then backed the main topsail. The most southern land in sight bearing South 3/4 East. We filled away. At dark, we signalled the boat to return.

We came to with the kedge in 16 fathoms water. We found a muddy bottom. The sails were furled. At 6, we got underway again and sounded in 17 fathoms water. At 11:30, we came to with the kedge and then sent the boats out again to sound. We found a strong current setting to the northeast. Sick report lists 17 men. Latitude 4.45 north/Longitude 114.18 east.

April 21, 1845 -- During this day the temperature is hot as hell. We have kept a boat out sounding shoals every few miles. We are schooling our waters very rapidly. Sometimes we find ourselves in 50 to 70 fathoms of water in 5 or 10 minutes which makes sailing a very ticklish affair. So far we have had only one rub. This is certainly good luck, but it is soon learned by sailors that the Captain makes all the difference. So far we have had excellent management. We have also found our charts sadly lacking in this area of the world and are busily employed correcting them. Distance made these 24 hours is 58 miles. Latitude 4.43 north/Longitude no entry.

April 22, 1845 -- During this day there is nothing but heat as usual. The sky is very clear and the water is a deep blue with blue mud at a depth of 45 fathoms. We barely discovered a shoal a few hundred yards directly ahead of us and had to abruptly tack the vessel. We sent out a boat for sounding and found only 13 fathoms. The lookouts were licked good by the Captain for not keeping a proper watch from the mast heads. We kept a boat out all night sounding. As soon as we had some daylight, the boat was hoisted back up and we made and reduced sail as the occasion required. Distance made these 24 hours is 44 miles. Sick report has 24 men. Latitude 4.53 north/Longitude 112.48 east.

April 26, 1845 -- We are experiencing very heavy squalls and fresh northeast trades. Several of the men have been thrown from their berths. At times the ship has appeared to be on her beams. We have shortened sail to topsails. The jib blew out of the bolt rope. We had a very sad incident with seaman John Thompson. While he was employed furling the topgallant, he fell overboard. In the rough sea, the men reported that he sunk as soon as he hit the water. The ship was braced and a boat lowered and a buoy cut for him, but to no avail as no body was found. We have been followed at times by large schools of dolphins but at other times by large shark. A man's life is over if he goes over in these seas. Distance made these 24 hours is 92 miles. Sick report lists 22 men. Latitude 6.50 north/Longitude 109.52 east.

April 28, 1845 -- We sent a boat out to examine a strange discoloring in the water and found a large squid near the ship. The northeast monsoons hang on with us. At 3 p.m., we crossed a large line of green and sounded in 58 fathoms of water. We could see large brig to the windward but could not make out the identity. Distance made these 24 hours is 29 miles. Latitude 9.14 north/Longitude 109.4 east.

May 1, 1845 -- The ship is under topgallant and topmast studding sails. We made and shortened sails as occasion required. Our bad weather continues as a faithful companion. Earlier in the morning we had a rather large school of dolphins and porpoises with us. Later in the day, we discovered an extremely large shark in company. Some of the crew offered him a large piece of pork, but his sharkship refused.

The health of the crew is generally improving except for the men who were severely stricken with dysentery. They are the only ones left on the list presently. Distance made these 24 hours is 35 miles. Sick list has 23 men. Latitude 10.23 north/Longitude 109.34 east.

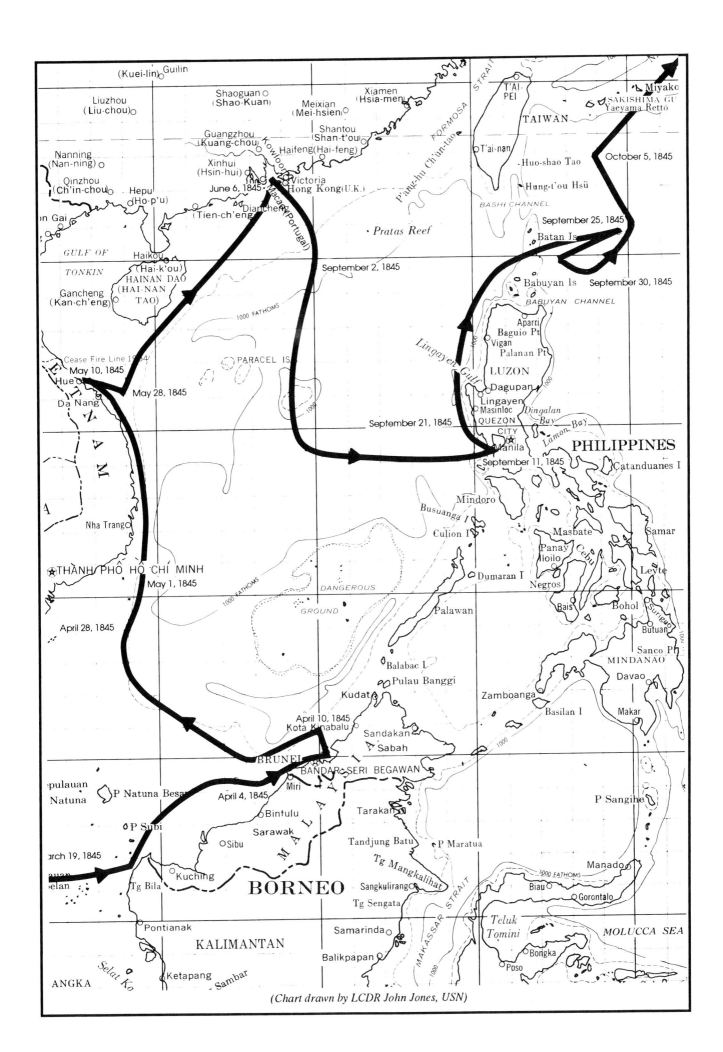

(Chart drawn by LCDR John Jones, USN)

May 2, 1845 -- The ship is under all plain sail. We made and shortened sail as situation required. During this day the water was covered with a very fine seaweed. At daylight, we discovered the high land of Cochin China. A Chinese junk and a bark were in sight to the west. The high land in sight to the north. Distance made these 24 hours is 51 miles. Latitude 10.47 north/Longitude 109.27 east.

May 3, 1845 -- The ship is under all plain sail on the wind. A strong current was found running to the south. There is a large quantity of sea weed or whales' feed drifting past the ship. There are now two sails astern. Most north land in sight at sunset bearing North 3/4 West. Distance made these 24 hours is 51 miles. Latitude 10.56 north/Longitude 109.24 east.

May 4, 1845 -- Today we finally mustered the entire crew and asked the Lord to provide us with a stiff breeze. The weather is so hot and almost to the point of being unbearable. All we can ask is that we make more than two miles a day. There are now several sails in sight. Distance made these 24 hours is 34 miles. Latitude 10.58 north/Longitude 109.34 east.

May 8, 1845 -- At 9, we came to with the kedge in 20 fathoms of water, soft blue mud. At 1, we got underway. There are several Chinese junks or pirate ships nearby. Land is in sight abeam to the westward. We were employed the latter part of the day in beating up to the windward, but going to the leeward. Latitude 15.16 north/Longitude 108.32 east.

May 9, 1845 -- During the day the weather was extremely hot and unpleasant. At 6, we anchored in 16 fathoms of water with blue mud. Cape Turon [Tourane is located on the coast of Vietnam, 40 miles southeast of the old provincial capital of Hue] is bearing north by west at a distance of 6 miles. At daylight we got underway again. We made all sail on the wind but went 10 miles to the leeward in the course of the day which was very distressing to all the crew since they were hard up for grub. Latitude 15.10 north/Longitude 108.32 east.

Off Cape Turon

May 10, 1845 -- The weather continues as hot as blazes. Today we have boarded two junks without any particular incident. Saw many of them standing out. We had to anchor and then get underway several times. All hands are employed in working into Turon Bay. Two boats were readied, manned and armed to visit the city of Turon. Upon entering the bay, the fort hoisted a black flag. As soon as the ship rounded the point, they hauled down the black flag and hoisted the Cochin China Flag. It was a yellow flag.

Turon Bay

May 11, 1845 -- The clouds around the mountains, together with the constantly entering and exiting junks, render the entire harbor into a peaceful scene. We finally ran into the harbor and anchored in 10 fathoms water.

[The harbor at Tourane is protected by two landfalls, Callo Han to the north, and Tun Tcheu to the south.]

The east end of Callao Han bore on the compass North by West 1/4 West. The outer extremity of the peninsula of Tun Tcheu bore East Southeast 1/2 East. The fort on the hill bore south by west. William Cook departed this life and we buried him on the peninsula. The burial service was read properly over him. The colors on board ship were half-masted. During the night, the watch reported that several large boats filled around us but none came close enough to board.

May 12, 1845 -- We shifted our anchor closer into the fort. All the boats were hoisted out to water the ship. A fishing boat suddenly pulled up alongside but no motion was given him to come aboard. He made a significant sign repeating at the same time Mandarin. All the while the sign was made by catching hold of his hair and chewing his finger and then taking it around as a knife would cut. After making this, he pulled away as fast as possible.

To the north and east of the fort, there is a small sandy beach about a yard wide. Then after that rises the tall green mountains of Tun Techeu. Down along the sides of this mountain flow several crystal clear streams to the beach. It was there that we sent our boats to water our ship. We collected the water in a hose tub. The hose lead from the tub directly into the casks.

Turon Bay lies open to the north and is almost a circle. It resembles Rio de Janeiro remarkably. Tall and singularly wild looking mountains lie on every side. The land breeze comes down from these peaks through the green valleys cool and bracing and so very refreshing to one who has been in the tropics for any length of time. The whole bay is shut in like an amphitheatre [almost encircled] except on the side to seaward and a barrow [sic] [barren] strip of sand to the southeast. The formation of these mountains is granite. In many places there are signs of volcanic action. In fact, the rocks on every shore show a vitrified appearance as if great heat had been applied to them. In many places the granite is round in appearance and are arranged in singular confusion. Clustering among them are vines so thick that one imagines himself in some well hid and chosen grove.

The country around the bay is very thickly populated and at places on the sea beach, villages can be found clustered near the water. The houses of the Cochin Chinese are built only one story high and of bamboo. The only bed that is used is a few mats. The dress of the Cochin Chinese is very loose trousers from the hips to the knees. They all have huge conical hats. The soldiers have a red gown or dress descending to their hips. The Mandarins wear a black silk gown and slippers. Many of the plainer folk wear a black silk gown and slippers, except the Mandarins' clothes are always very much finer and cleaner kept.

We usually took in about 5,000 gallons of water per day. There were three large ships laying in close to the land and housed over. They are said to belong to the King at Hue. They mount about 16 guns each.

One day during our stay, the Mandarins paid us a visit. Amongst them was somebody who shyly gave the Captain a letter. Nothing at that moment was said or done. The letter was not read until the Mandarins left the ship. On reading it, we found out that it was from the French Missionary, Dominique Lefevre.

He was the Bishop of Isamapolis and apostolic vicar of Cochin China. He said in his letter that he was confined in a dungeon and was condemned to die. He begged us to make haste thinking also that we were French. He begged us to hasten or it would certainly be too late.

The Captain ordered a boat armed and manned immediately. This was done with great dispatch and an expedition of eighty armed men left the ship.

[Ship's Clerk B.F. Stevens wrote the following report on the situation:

"Here was the predicament. A Frenchman was at the mercy of the barbarians. He was a Christian and humanity called for our assistance. No French ships were in the harbor and France and America were on the best of terms.

"Before assistance could be obtained from Canton he would probably be executed, as the postscript of his letter implied. The instructions of our government to the Captain ordered him to offer any assistance or aid to citizens of other nations that he might meet during the cruise and I think this was a case in point. Should we set aside the claims of humanity? These people respect no civilized powers, will make no treaties and are destitute of all faith in keeping even the slightest promise. Their conduct to us, though not actually uncivil, implied a direct and groundless suspicion of our character, though the authorities in Turon had been repeatedly assured that we were a national vessel, only requiring water and refreshments, and willing and ready to pay for whatever received."]

[Thomas journal continues:]

Captain Percival led the expedition which also consisted of some thirty marines. The company landed and proceeded to the town. Soldiers and marines were posted from the landing to the house where a meeting was arranged. The Captain demanded the Frenchman and some time to secure his safety and the Captain stated that they would also do everything desired of them for his release.

Receiving no satisfaction, the expedition returned to the warship with three captured hostages. They were Mandarins. After delaying for three or four days, three men-of-war junks came out of the river and anchored near the ship under the land. When they came up they were filled with soldiers. Soldiers were also landed all morning long on the beach. [At this point, Thomas discontinues using dates during the Vietnam segment.] On Sunday morning, we prepared, manned and armed three boats. About three o'clock they left the ship under the protection of our guns. While we were doing this we were in musket shot of the three junks and also of the fort on the hill. Yet, a single shot was not fired even though everything was prepared and readied. So far not one man on the expedition had been harmed.

Some of our marines boarded one of the junks. The junk's captain and his men seemed taken by surprise and appeared to have just awoke. The captain was seen to take a tompkin of a gun and hastily put it back again. We found a leather box at hand with 8 to 10 cartridges, a few shots and a wad at hand, etc.

Each of these three junks was armed with 3 to 5 small 6 lb. cannon. Some were brass and others iron. On the same evening of our boarding raid, we noticed the Cochin Chinese clearing away the thatch and getting their ships ready for sea.

Soon after, a messenger came onboard with a letter as long as my arm. The whole subject of the letter was why we had come here, why they did not go to our country, and asking why we catch their Mandarins, as they do not catch ours. The Mandarins, the letter went on to read, were very much alarmed.

We then hauled up the ship to within a mile and one third of the town. The guns were prepared for action and an expedition was readied. The crew was beat to

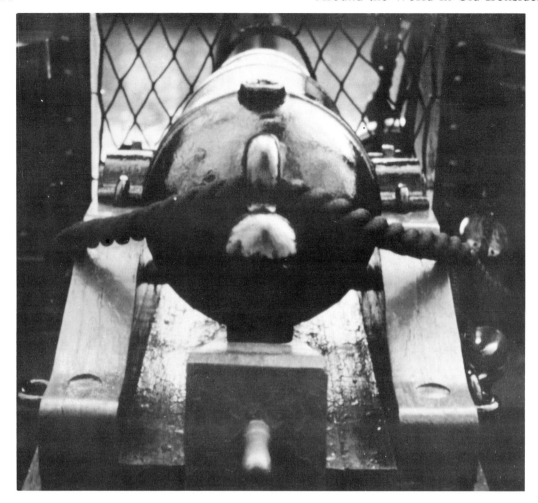

Close up of a Constitution gun (Photo by Alan Flanders).

quarters. The expedition was well armed and under our guns went up to the town. Captain Percival led the forces and expected to find the Frenchman there. He accordingly took one of the principal [sic] Mandarin hostages with him. There was much talk among the reefers that they were walking into a trap. A boat was stationed off the river to make signals in case of danger. There were now 11 armed junks pulling to and fro in the river and about 200 soldiers drawn up about the town.

After a long stay at the town engaged in corresponding with the Mandarins, the boats returned. We fired several of our cannon at this time to try their ranges. There were many fishing boats pulling out from the river at the same time. At the sound of Old Ironsides's guns, they all pulled back. We fired all together 10 shells. The Cochin Chinese ships got up their topmasts and lower yards and spent the rest of the day, the 22nd., loading guns.

The fort, at the mouth of the river, was nearly dismantled to supply the ships with guns. We could also observe every soldier at the fort busily employed fortifying every pass and landing place. There was no doubt now that they were ready for a fight.

These events made things look very serious and our hostages began to beg us to place them ashore. They promised that if we complied with their wishes, they would see to it that the Frenchman would be set free in three days. As there was no reason to keep them, we released them. Of course, they told a lie.

We found a junk the next day making curious movements around the ship so we sent a boarding party over to it. We found that the Mandarins had visited them and placed wooden collars around the neck of the captain and pitch plasters over their eyes. When we tried to help remove them, the poor devils said no and made a sign that the Mandarins would cut off their heads if the plasters were removed.

A messenger came onboard with a letter dated the 20th. The same day, the clouds began to lower around the mountains till they were only a few hundred feet from the water. It was so hot that I decided to try and cook an egg in the sun which I did by placing it on my hammock cloth and blocking it. Since the air temperature was now a constant 90 degrees the egg was soon ready to eat and this was near one of the ports [ventilation openings or hatchways on the ship].

In the morning and during the latter part of the night it blew quite strong with rain. Our junk, that we had captured, suddenly got underway and ran for the river. We fired 9 shots at and across their bow. We next sent an armed boat to cut them out. They were found to be still making all sail up the river. One of them was brought to and boarded. [Apparently there were then at least three armed junks in range of the Constitution.] Our men forcibly anchored her at the mouth of the river and there being rough seas, several were seen to drown. The wind continued to blow furiously, and on a long sandy spit that runs out from the mouth of the river, there was a good deal of surf and a few large breakers. Some of our boats were very near swamping.

After the boats were brought to some safety, they proceeded up the river in quest of the runaways. The runaways were found filled with soldiers. Our man also found anchored among them ten very heavily armed junks. Several of them had our boats in aim. When we got closer to them, we left our guns so as not to portray our real strength and all the men were ordered to draw cutlasses. When they boarded, the

Constitution guns sound off (Photo by Margie J. Shaw, courtesy of USN).

natives at first seized their arms and then suddenly threw them down. As our men boarded on one side, the natives jumped overboard on the other.

The whole shore was lined with soldiers and all our fire arms were wet. Our men had also covered some in hopes of fooling the enemy which worked for the boarding party. We now thought that the soldiers and forts would surely open fire upon us. Since we were now surrounded, there was nothing left to do but land our forces. Our men cheered savagely and then charged them. They broke and ran like sheep.

Our boats were soon able to get underway and tow out the prizes. They soon anchored near the ship. That night it blew a gale.

On the 23rd., we commenced watering the ship. There was no particular incident. On the 24th., we decided that there was no use delaying off Turon any longer. We sent a boat in with a letter for the Mandarins. It was returned with an answer that if we behaved ourselves and gave up the junks, etc., the Frenchman would be released.

On the 25th., the junks were released. We then sent a boat for the poor missionary who is said to be confined with a pair of irons on his legs and one on his thighs, and one on his arms. There is also an iron around his neck and an iron bar connecting all of it. This was a story told by a Cochin Chinese who spoke Portuguese.

We did not get him as they broke their word. The ship was hauled up to the watering place as it was now too dangerous for the smaller boats to go too far from the ship. Wood was also obtained from the natives at a very moderate price. On the 27th., with little chance of freeing Bishop Lefevre, we sailed from Turon. The Captain had decided on first opportunity to get word to the French authorities of the Bishop's plight.

The entire crew left Turon safely. It was tragic that such a beautiful area could possess such danger. Turon Bay is truly one of the most beautiful bays in the entire world. I wish that a Walter Scott could be amongst these wild and rugged mountains to describe them. It would be remarkable to see him describe the customs and superstitions of these wild natives of the mountains. From them, we had found little difficulty in getting fresh fowl, potatoes, eggs, etc. The entrance of the bay lies open to the north and there is little difficulty in entering. There is plenty of water to within 1/4 of a mile of either of those for a frigate as far up as 1/2 mile inside of the fort on the hill at the entrance. The bottom is muddy and very good holding ground. Water is abundant and easily obtainable.

At the bottom of the Bay is a fine site for a large city. There is a large hill of beautiful marble which can easily be seen. It is called Marble Rock. Sugar is raised in great abundance, but not as an export.

On the 28th., we fired a few shells by way of experiment on Calloo Han Isle [minor island within Tourane Bay] at a distance of about 2 miles. Two of our shells burst in the air and the rest fell short in the water. During our stay, there was a sea breeze every day. We painted the ship black instead of the lead color. The pitch had begun to run out of the seams.

On the day we left Cochin China, a ship crossed the topgallant yards and showed twelve guns on each side. Three other brigs came in from the direction of Hue Mountains with 10 guns each and anchored near the fort. The Captain led a party of men to board one of them. At first they tried to keep him off with spears through their ports and from over their sides. The Captain, however, mounted the side with pistol in one hand. He seated himself on the quarterdeck. All the Chinese rushed forward with alarm. After taking a good look around, he pushed off and came back onboard.

Cochin China is an extensive and rich country. It adjoins and is forced to pay tribute to the Emperor of China. Hue is the Capital of the Kingdom and is a strongly fortified place having over 2,000 guns mounted around the city. The King is a despot and has absolute power over every man, woman and child in the Kingdom. To communicate bad news to him, is to commit high treason. Their religion is said to be

Buddhism or a belief in the Genih Devil. In every village, we saw one house built better than all the rest. This was the Jos-House. The Jos-House was the shrine of all their idols and their priest. Strangers are not allowed to travel through the country. White elephants are held in great respect here as they are thought to hold the spirit of the past kings.

The soldiers are usually armed with spears or muskets and at the town were two large forts capable of mounting 11 guns. A frigate can haul up to within 1 and 1/2 miles of these forts. During our stay, we saw but few women. When we went to any of the villages, the women would hide and the youngsters would run off and scream if we came near them. What few women I did see were ugly as sin and only one appeared decent and she was selling a pig. On this day we also experienced a total eclipse of the moon.

May 28, 1845 -- At 6:20 p.m., Calloo Han bore on the compass south by east, Goat Island is south southwest 1/2 west. At 7, we sounded in 27 fathoms of water with a bottom of soft blue mud. We made and shortened sail as occasion required. Land in sight. A large number of fishing boats out with us. We can also easily make out a large group of junks with them. The high land of Cochin China is in sight to the south and west. Latitude 16.14 north/Longitude 108.50 east.

May 29, 1845 -- There are several small sail in sight. We pass often very near the fishing boats. Today we have managed to board one of them and have brought back a large mess of flying fish that are so plentiful in these waters. The crew is busily employed painting a white streak. [During the voyage, experiments with various hull paints were carried out to determine their durability and insulation qualities.] Distance made these 24 hours is 30 miles. Latitude 17.12 north/Longitude 109.32 east.

May 30, 1845 -- At daylight, we could see the island of Hainan [located in the Gulf of Tonkin, part of China] on the weather bow. A ship was discovered on the starboard quarter. We showed our colors. The painters are still employed in their work. The sailmakers are engaged in making a new foresail. We have once more seen a large number of fishing boats. This area seems like a Newfoundland to the Chinese.

Ship's Clerk B.F. Stevens reported that he learned on the morning of the 30th., after we boarded an English ship from Singapore, headed for Hong Kong, with a French priest onboard, that the French squadron was at Singapore. It was also learned that M. Lefevre's imprisonment was known, and the French admiral was ordered to proceed to Turon Bay "to effect his liberation."

[Recognition by the French government of the Constitution's timely intervention on behalf of Bishop Lefevre was complicated by political unrest in Paris with the exile of King Louis Philippe who was on the throne during the event.]

June 4, 1845 -- The ship is now under starboard studding sail. The crew was inspected at quarters. At daylight, land was just ahead. At meridian, the Ladrone Isle is in sight to the north and west. At 10 a.m., we received a pilot on board from Macao [major 19th century Portuguese trading center on the coast of Canton, China]. During the remainder of the day, we stood in for the roads of Macoa. Distance made these 24 hours is 93 miles. Sick list is 28 men. Latitude 21.28 north/Longitude 113.32 east.

Off Macao

June 6, 1845 -- We are standing in for Macao. Boarded an American Ship, the Rainbow, which was homeward bound, and sent a mail bag by her to the United States. [The Rainbow, designed in 1845 by John W. Griffiths, was considered by many to be the prototype of the American nineteenth century large extreme clipper which incorporated many advanced ideas. She had a tragic end just three years later when she was reported missing with all hands.] At 7 p.m., we came to with the larboard anchor in 5 1/4 fathoms and veered to with the 15 fathom chain. We boarded the American Barque Caqua which was 14 days from Singapore.

June 7, 1845 -- We received the tragic notice of Commodore Dallas. [Commodore Dallas was commander of American naval forces operating off of Mexico where the Constitution was destined.] The colors were halfmasted and we fired 13 guns as a mark of respect.

June 8, 1845 -- Shifted our berth further to the east. We then fired a salute of 21 guns to the Portuguese flag which was answered by the fort on the shore. All hands were called to muster for Divine Services. The Articles of War were read. We also received a reprimand from the Navy Department to the finding of a court martial held on passed Midshipman E. Higgins for disobedience of orders. The American Counselor agent came on board.

Macao

June 9, 1845 -- We filled up stores from the navy store and also received a boat load of water. A party of officers left the ship for Canton. We boarded the Ann

Maria of Salem from Singapore. A letter bag was sent to the United States by the Venice. Joshua Greenwood, Charles Brown, and George Lewis were shipped. We are busy receiving all types of supplies and restocking the bread stores. The crews of the first cutters were punished for drunkenness and smuggling liquor.

A number of men were discharged as foreigners at their requests. On the 18th., the ship was underway for the entrance of the Canton River and Boca Tigris [a strait in the Canton River]. We boarded and sent a letter bag to the United States by the Aquelness to New York. As we were standing in for the forts, the ship was run in a mud bank. We braced back and let go the larboard anchor. The ship did not get free until 8:30; we finally got underway with all drawing sails and stood up the river. The sick report is now at 34 men. At 12:30, we came to on June 20th., after having arrived in anchorage.

We were moored with 40 fathoms on each chain. The royal yards were sent down. Air temperature is around 88 degrees.

[The following section is an excellent example of nineteenth century intelligence reports on a foreign port of great interest to the United States. A major part of the Constitution's mission, as stipulated by their underway orders, was to gather such information.]

Macao is a Portuguese city and like all their cities is heavily fortified. The city is also walled. It is situated on a peninsula and had at one time much trade. It was the depot of Chinese and European goods. Lately other places have gone ahead of Macao in every respect. The city, from the water, looks beautiful, but its beauty is destroyed on going through the streets by their narrowness and filth. The streets are so irregular that it is very difficult to find your way around them. The Chinese here are the most numerous class and are the workmen and artisans of the place. They far surpass the Portuguese in industry and many other things. The Governor lives in Macao as well.

There is a strong garrison in Macao and their presence can easily be detected. Some of them are fine looking men. As Macao is a very old place, two or three hundred years old, there has been a gradual mixture of half and half girls with the Portuguese and many are naturally related. There are some half dozen forts advantageously situated with many brass pieces mounted around the town. There is no doubt, that if attacked, the stout hearts of Macao could make a brave defense. On the land side there is a strong wall and in part of this wall are numerous rice fields with narrow causeways and marshy beds for rice. These areas could easily be defended. Then further out still, the peninsula narrows less than 250 yards. No one can doubt but that this pass could be denied to any enemy force.

There are a great number of churches in Macao for its size. I was on shore one Sunday, and could scarcely count the bells that appeared to be ringing around me. I saw several Asiatic Jews or Parsees. [During the nineteenth century, the "Parsees" were an important element of international trade throughout the Middle East and the Orient, having mastered the language of most Europeans and understanding the social and business customs of their place of business.] They are a business set of men and all that I have seen appear in very neat dress. We all have a respect for them.

One of the prettiest sights in Macao is at sundown. It was quite a pleasure to go down to the green near the fort, and look down and listen to the children playing and singing their hearts out amongst laughter and shouts of joy. About sundown, all the nurses of the white children bring out their young masters. Many of the mistresses on the green are very beautiful and there are some very handsome boys as well. They spoke in a very strange language that I took to be Portuguese. No sailor can see them, less he thinks of home and of his own school boy days.

Macao, to the best of my knowledge, was founded in 1553. It is not as generally supposed controlled and property of the Portuguese, but rather they hold the area by the permission granted to them by the Emperor. Sick report lists 31 men.

Blenheim Beach

[Blenheim Beach was located across the Canton River, north of Macoa near the 19 century British trading center of Victoria.]

June 21 to July 1, 1845 -- During this interval, we had a shower every other day and continued to load provisions. The mosquitos are too thick to get a proper breath. We filled up with water from the river. We used a new method of cleaning it. All the water was filtered through charcoal sponges. It was very good. (The obvious success of the ship's new water filter system was a major breakthrough for the Navy.) The slings of the fore and main yards were shortened and the ratlines were squared. We boarded several American Ships: the Sappho, Akbar, and Horatio.

July 1 to July 31, 1845 -- On July 4th., we fired a 21 gun salute in honor of the day. The main brace was spliced. A ration of rum was served in celebration. The H.B.M. Castor arrived from Hong Kong. We exchanged salutes. On July 17th., Charles Lewis, the captain of the fore deck, died. He was buried on shore as the band played the dead march. On July 22nd., Charles Chrohon died and was buried on shore as well. He was from Norfolk, Virginia. His messmates and many friends attended the burial.

The carpenters are employed in repairing the boats damaged in the fighting in Cochin, China. On the 31st., we unbent the sails and unmoored the ship. The topgallant yards were crossed short as the ship was dropped down the river. We received a pilot onboard. At 9 a.m., the anchor was hauled up and sails made as we stood for the mouth of the river. Sick report has 59 men.

August 1 to August 25, 1845 -- The 1st., 2nd., and 3rd. boats are employed in dropping down to Boca Tigris. The American Steamer Midas is following in case we need assistance. The 3rd. boat came to anchor near the French Frigate Cleopatra.

[The next landfalls of Wantong and Chuen on the Canton River were fortified by the French as noted by Thomas.]

We moored the ship. The round forts on the south Wantong bore a compass reading of north. The tower on Chuen bore East by South 3/4 South. Tycock point bore South Southeast 1/2 East. Tiger Island bore Northwest by North. We exchanged salutes with the French Admiral.

The Cleopatra is said to have brought official letters thanking Captain Percival for his intercession at Turon Bay in behalf of Bishop Lefevre. On August 3rd., Captain Percival addressed the crew. The subject of the speech concerned the large and growing number of sick men among the crew. He said that even though many were ill, the crew had no reason to despond and that they must keep up a good heart. He also added that we would return home as soon as duty allowed us. He also spoke for the first time of the rumors of a possible war [with Mexico]. He said that he hoped that the rumors were untrue, but that if they were not, he had every confidence in the ship's company.

Boca Tigris

[Boca Tigris was another principal French trading center on the Canton River.]

We found the weather considerably cooler but it was still hot as blazes. We have had a shower of rain every day. On August 9th., we heard about the Princeton calamity. A subscription was caused onboard of about $2,000, for the sufferers. On August 12th., we employed a large Chinese boat to water the ship. We sent 48 casks and beakers by cutter with Swift in charge. On the 13th., Henry Lehman departed this life and on the 24th., George Fulcher died after a short illness. On the 25th., we bent the sails, and crossed the topgallant yards. The French Flag was hoisted at the fore. Every other day, we received fresh provisions for the crew.

August 25 to September 1, 1845 -- I have observed that after a thunder storm, it was always cooler. This is the southwest monsoon yet the wind generally blows from the east or south and east. The reason I suppose is this: that the southwest monsoon is gradually drawn out of its course by the heated land to the west. On August 27th., we got underway from Boca Tigris. We came to on the 28th., with the starboard anchor and veered to the 30 fathoms chain. Pilot Island bore south 1/4 west. The city of Macao bore Northwest by West 3/4 West. All are busily preparing the ship for sea.

Blenheim Beach is almost 15 miles from the city of Canton. The land on each side of the river is low, immediately adjoining the river, and is covered with rice. There are several large villages nearby. There is one in the bend of the river and it is remarkable for its curious tomb stones. They are monumental in appearance. There are also several large and tall pagodas in sight and one or two large forts. The river here is quite muddy and also has a very strong current. We filled up with water from the river and used our charcoal filter to clean it.

The scenery around Blenheim Beach is very pretty. The river is always full of boats and our ship was continually surrounded with beggars. They kept up a noise by yelling for some "chow chow."

The English Frigate, which lies very near, is called the Castor and is beautiful. She mounts 28 long guns and 32 cannon on her gun deck. She was kept in fine condition and was a regular out and out ship. The Castor took in $2,000,000.00 in treasure which was the last payment in Chinese indemnity. Her gun deck was laid diagonally. Every day they exercised their men with both the ship gun exercise and the handspike exercise. They also worked on their ability to use small arms, swords and cutlasses. The English are in such a secular position that it is essentially necessary that she should have a well drilled and disciplined marine.

Canton is as everyone knows a large business and wealthy city. I was informed on good authority that it contained 1,300,000 inhabitants. The river town lies above Canton proper. Tis said it contains some 80,000 boats and 400,000 inhabitants. These boats are arranged in streets, etc. on shore. Whole families occupy these boats; they never go onshore except in case of extreme necessity. This may appear singular but there are laws against their coming ashore.

Some of these boats are remarkable for their beauty and many are kept very clean. Besides beauty, they are built with great skill, many are curved and painted and then gilded. The interiors of some are filled with splendors. Large lamps, soft cushions and carpets of the most beautiful workmanship give them such an air of complete luxury. The suburbs of Canton are as large as the city within the walls. There is but little difference between the buildings outside of the walls and those inside.

The streets inside the walls are narrower and the houses lower than those outside. When once through the wall, the crowds would surprise any American. Everyone has to elbow along sideways as best he can. Besides this, the boys follow and shout "Fanqui Low" [sic] [foreign devil] and throw stones at foreigners.

One thing that particularly struck me was the behavior of the Chinese children. I never saw them at play of any kind and seldom saw them cry. On the river all the children have a gourd lashed on their backs to prevent them from drowning.

At the Bogue or Boca Tigris are extensive forts. It is said that there are over 2,000 guns mounted around the mouth of the river. In the middle of the river, at the Bogue, are two islands. These are almost covered by forts. Yet, the forts are badly built or rather constructed so that they could be easily taken by European forces. They are so constructed that the guns in them cannot be trained.

The hills are quite high and some of them are bare. They contrast with the walls of Chinese forts since the hills are black while the forts all have white walls.

The Chinese have many guns of their own manufacture but they are clumsy things. The carriages of all of their guns are worthless for they are very frail so that they will be destroyed by the recoil of their own guns. In Canton there are many fine and large buildings. The colleges [public grade school] open to everybody so that it is seldom one meets with a Chinese who can not read and write. The only way to office and elevation in China is by learning. A learned man is everywhere respected.

Police officers are very numerous and are also very efficient. Every province in China is sub-divided amongst the police. Each one is responsible to his superior for the good behavior of his part. Every housekeeper is responsible for the order of his own home. A Police officer is assigned ten houses to look out for. Each householder is then responsible to the Police officer. This Police officer is responsible to the one who has one hundred houses and up the ladder of command to the one who has one thousand and then to the Viceroy and finally the Viceroy to the Emperor himself.

A street in Canton is worth visiting as almost anything can be obtained. The finest silks are exposed for sale. The most curious works of bone and ivory are displayed. In Canton there is also a very fine glass factory. The glass they make is somewhat inferior to others I have seen.

On the 5th. day of the 5th. moon, I was in Canton for the feast of the great dragon. It was an interesting sight. The great dragon is a kind of water god and on or about this time the Chinese feast and sacrifice. The principal place of amusement during the dragon feast is on the water which is alive with beautiful boats. There is singing, music and much amusement. There were 8 or 10 large dragon boats on the river. These boats or canoes were from 80 to 120 feet long and only about 2 feet wide. They were pulled about with short paddles on each and amidship were gongs, fireworks, dancers, whilst everyone in the boat kept time with the music with their paddles, and voices. The flower boats were on this day rigged up in a beautiful style. Everyone appeared to try and see how much voice they could make and how well they could enjoy themselves.

Above the town is a large garden and during the celebration, a large feast was spread for anyone who wished to partake. One of the curious things on the river is the great number of rafts and the thousands of ducks about them. They fend for themselves and come and go as they are called. Many of the fishermen have trained hawks to fish for them. These hawks will sometimes fly off a mile or two, take a fish and return with it in the boat. The river at Canton is not more than one-half mile in width, but it is very deep. The Jos House, or temple, in Canton are large and fine. Some of them are very splendidly filled up and for their curious workmanship are very worth visiting.

The River Yantze Kiang or the Son of the Sea, is a large river and runs through China from west to east. It is second in size only to the Mississippi, and the Amazon. A few hundred miles above its mouth, it takes the name of the Golden Sanded. This river runs through the largest lake in China known by the name of the Tong Ling Hoo [Tungting]. It is a beautiful lake, surrounded by high mountains with wild scenery. Around its shores and amongst the mountains live the wild Macoutre. These are the only people in China who will not acknowledge the Emperor. They do not wear their hair as the rest of the Chinese but rather allow it to grow long over the whole head. Whilst the Chinese will shave all but a long curl.

The Grand Canal of China is said to be about 600 miles, but a quarter part of it is nothing but a banked up creek, the banks of which require a great deal of repairing. Where this canal enters the Yellow River is a superb temple to the Great Dragon or the Father of the Waters. The canal passes near the city of Hang-Fou and is so much above it that passengers may look down on the roof of houses of the city in passing it.

The Chinese have accounts of a great deluge which took place 4,000 years ago, yet, they say it only impeded agriculture. They also record that the celebrated Yu, who is deified by them, let off the water by nine great channels. The City of Peking [then the capital of the Empire of China, about 60 miles south of the Great Wall and the border of Mongolia] contains about 3 million people, but I expect the account is exaggerated.

The walls of Peking are 33 miles in circumference. The houses are built only one story high. When the Emperor was shown pictures of European houses 8 or 9 stories tall, he asked why the foreigners or Fanquis built their houses so high. Was it not enough, he asked, to live alongside of each other that people chose to live above one another.

Near Peking are the Emperor's gardens which are today in a dilapidated state, yet, they still possess a semblance of their former beauty. They are built after the Chinese fashion and cultivated according to their taste accompanied by the usual representation of ruins, rocks, artificial lakes, etc.

Hang Chou [Hangchow, located south of Shanghai, at the eastern extremity of Hangchow Bay] is the greatest silk city of China. It lies in about 30 degrees north. The finest silk country lies between 30 degrees and 35 degrees north. Hoo Chou Fou [location and present name of Hoo Chou Fou and Ming Po are unknown] is the great tea city. Near it is the great city of Ming Po. Tis said Ming Po is the second largest city in China. The masts of the junks there resemble a great forest. Thousands of boats are continually pulling on the river either for business or pleasure. Near Ming Po is the great tea country. It is in sight of the Bashea Hills from which the Bashea tea is taken.

In west China, Tibet cows flourish and are valuable because of its tail where extremely fine hair may be taken. From these tails are manufactured beautiful shawls, carpets, etc. There is one place where an oily substance oozes from the ground. The Chinese call this stone oil and burn it in their lamps.

In the west of China, tea is used as a medium of exchange. In China, the laws and customs have so regulated it that a farmer is the most respectable of men, whilst a merchantman is looked on as almost nobody. This is as it should be, for those who feed the nation are the most useful and the most independent, and therefore, the most respectable.

Paternal authority is the model of Chinese life. A father has the power of life and death over his children and he is responsible for their actions. He may also be punished for the crimes or misdeeds of his children. Respectability is carried to a great extreme through the Chinese Emperor. Every father is responsible for his family and every Mandarin [a public position of high office under the Chinese Empire] is responsible for his province. To have a rebellion in a province is considered a crime. The Vice Roy is punished for this whether he had a part in it or not. The Emperor is considered to be the father of the Empire. He is therefore responsible to God and the whole nation for his actions. Once a year, the Emperor ploughs a piece of land to encourage the farmers. He is sometimes termed the divine husbandman. He is also termed the celestial father.

The Chinese are an unwarlike race and not giving to dissipation or fighting. They are also remarkable for their wants of patriotism. I think with proper management, an army could be raised and disciplined from amongst the Chinese that would equal any army in the world. My reasons for thinking this are that they are a very obedient people. They are robust and no doubt possess much animal courage. The Emperor in his dispatches says that he wishes to render the Empire filial to insure that all offenses against parents are severely punished.

We saw a young man, who struck his mother, put to death. His father was also put to a cruel death for allowing it. His mother was publicly cursed, his name was outlawed and the house where they lived was uprooted and the spot they lived on was cursed forever.

The bamboo is the instrument used in punishing criminals. A wooden collar is sometimes used. While the criminal wears this, he cannot free himself. The Chinese exercise the burial service with great solemnity and on a certain day of every year, they visit the grave of their father. There they burn incense, offer prayers and leave a gay pennant of silk over the grave. This is a pretty custom and shows the respect and honor their father received while he was alive.

New Year's Day is a great day with them. All business is suspended and for a week beforehand visits are received and feasts are given. An incessant crash of fireworks is kept up for a week or ten days. Shortly after New Year's Day, they celebrate the Feast of the Lanterns. On this day, everyone tries to produce a beautiful lantern. Some of them are remarkable for their curious construction and beauty. During the night, all the lanterns are hung up and of course give the city a beautiful appearance. To Europeans, the Chinese seem to be composed of an infinite number of contradictions.

A gentleman writing from Macao says on getting into the boat to leave the ship, he asked the boatman what course Macao lay. He replied east south (northwest). On asking him the direction of the wind he replied east south (southeast). Observing that he was dressed in white, I thought there must be a gay celebration commencing. So I asked him why he did dress so gay and he replied that his mother and father had just died. He said that he was in mourning. I was certainly shocked by that revelation and resolved to be more careful.

Once on shore, I saw a grave looking person in a long petticoat with a large fan. I inquired who it was. I was answered that the person was a high ranking military officer. I was still more astonished when I saw him mount his horse on the right side. A little further on, I saw two boys disputing about an orange. After a great deal of talk and gestulation, they at last sat down and divided it evenly between them. An English or American boy would have fought on for it. As I walked some distance on, I saw an old Chinese flying a kite. It was said that he had the ability to talk to birds and mice. A number of Chinese children were seriously watching him with their arms folded. Resolving to learn all that I could, and not to be surprised another time, I employed a Chinese master to teach me their language.

He commenced his discourse by saying that there was no alphabet as there is in English. He then took down a work, praised the merits of the author and read the title page. Saying it was written in the 5th. year, the 10th. month, and the 23rd. day, but wonder at my surprise if you choose, but he opened the book at the beginning as he said which I had always been taught was the end of the book.

He read from the right down the page, and so kept backwards, as we would call it, to the left. He then proceeded to instruct me in the manners and read from a page that when a friend comes to visit you, always place him on the left hand as it is the seat of honor. I also heard that you should always take your hat off in front of superiors or before those whom you respect, for it is indecent to expose your person before them and highly improper. He then proceeded to state that all great philosophers had agreed that the seat of the mind is in the stomach. He said that all young men should endeavor to appear decent. There, they should keep clean and always have their shoes well whitened. Also, when invited to a feast or to a dinner, you should always show that you relished the fare by belching at the table for this means that you have eaten too much, but that you found the meal so good that you could not stop eating.

I found generally the Chinese to be the reverse of the Europeans. They sail their boats small end first, read their books backwards, whiten their shoes, wear their stockings and shirts outside of their trousers, build their forts backwards as it were, and having a thousand little customs directly opposite to ours. On their religion there is little known for there are so many sects through the land and all are tolerated except the Christian Religion. The Chinese think that religion is a secondary thing and view it only as a beautiful study.

The population of China is said to be 300,000,000. This is nearly half the population of the entire world. Peace has reigned in China for 200 years. The people of China are the most cheerful, industrious and enterprising in Asia. This speaks well for their government.

Many Christian missionaries have been sent to China to teach, but my opinion is that these missionaries had better stay at home for the Christian natives are the most quarrelsome in the world and the Chinese the most peaceable. Such was the dread that the Chinese bear for Christians that they are forbidden it by the Emperor. The Emperor said that they will produce war and trouble and a Chinese maxim is that it is better to be a dog in peace than a man in trouble. Their criminal law is founded on the maxim that it is better to let the guilty escape than to punish the innocent.

September 1, 1845 -- During this day, the first part had light airs and the latter part had moderate breezes and pleasant weather. At daylight, we got underway and stood out of Macao Roads under all plain sail. At 8, Potoi Island bore compass reading of North 1/2 East. The outer extremity of great Ladione bore East Southeast 3/4 East. We unbent the sheet cable and shotted the guns.

The anchors were then secured for sea. We could see a man-of-war and a steamer in sight. There was also a Brig in sight; it appeared to be standing in for Macao. Latitude 21.34 south/Longitude 113.50 east.

September 2, 1845 -- During this day we have experienced moderate breezes and some squally weather. We made and reduced sail as occasion required. The ship is under royals and flying jib. The latter part of the night we reduced sail to a single reefed topsail. The mainsail was hauled up. The crew was busily employed pumping the ship out. The crew was then inspected at 9. We spotted a sail to the west. The day ended with mist and rain. Distance made these 24 hours is 139 miles. Latitude 19.51 north /Longitude 115.04 east.

September 5, 1845 -- We had to back sail the ship several times today. Clewed down the topgallant sails to a squall. Overhauled a number of bales of slop clothing and found them in good order. At 9, the crew was inspected at quarters. The ship was pumped out once again. We bent a new main sail. The spanker was repaired. The topgallants were furled to a heavy squall of wind and rain. Distance made these 24 hours is 101 miles. Sick list has 29 men. Latitude 16.21 north/Longitude 118.35 east.

September 6, 1845 -- At 9, the crew was mustered. The crew was assigned to quarters and exercised the great guns. The new main royal yard rope was roved [the end of a rope was passed through a hole in a block, cleat, etc.]. We also prepared a new cross jack brace and a new main bunt whip and larboard main leachline. The sailmakers have finished a new foresail. Crossed the royal yards. The ship is under plain sail. Distance made 45 miles. Sick list has 28 men. Latitude 16.34 north/Longitude 118.45 east.

September 7, 1845 -- We wore the ship to the south and the east. The ship is under royals and flying jib. At daylight, we discovered land in sight. It was bearing east by north. We also could make out two sails in sight. Their sighting was made off the weather bow. At 8 a.m., a large ship, two steamers and three smaller boats were in sight, also on the weather bow. At 10, we called all hands to muster and performed a divine service. At 11, we showed our colours to an English fleet consisting of 6 sails. They were made up of a line of battleships, a sloop of war, two brigs and two steamers. Distance made 56 miles. Latitude 15.08 north/Longitude 118.51 east.

September 8, 1845 -- The British Squadron bore down on us. At 1, the steamers raised steam and came alongside us. We beat to quarters and cleared the ship for action.

[Ship's Clerk B.F. Stevens recorded the following events:

"As the Constitution was slowly drifting along towards the port of Manila somewhat before daylight, or rather as the light began to appear, we found ourselves nearly surrounded by a squadron of European men-of-war, say twelve or fifteen of them, but whether British, French, Spanish or otherwise, could not be ascertained. As we had been a number of months without hearing from home, any guess as to our surroundings was as good as another, but the look about them was in the eyes of some old salts onboard unmistakenly English.

"One of the floating vessels bore an Admiral's pennant, afterwards ascertained to be the flag of Sir Thomas Cochrane, Commander of the China Squadron. The others were frigates, sloops, and brigs. They had evidently paid Manila a visit and were making their way to some port in the Pacific. As a matter of precaution the Constitution -- the favorite ship of our Navy -- was got ready for action, or rather put in a state of defense; it would never have done in any event to give up 'Old Ironsides' to any nation than the one which built her and had fought her.

"The officers and crew were at their stations, the wind was dead calm, watch fires were lighted, the magazines were opened and every preparation was made to show that we did not mean to give up the ship without struggle or show of defense. And thus things went on from the discovery of the drifting fleet until the time came round to make ourselves known, when the Star Spangled Banner was hove to the breeze, or what little of it there was, and the flag of Old England became unfurled at the masts of our neighbors.

"After a short delay, a boat put off from the Admiral's ship and approached the Constitution, and a young officer climbed the side of our ship and stepped on the frigate's deck. Captain Percival, who was waiting with the First Lieutenant, Amasa Paine, of Providence, Rhode Island, to receive him, said, 'Is it peace or war?' 'Why, to be peace for sure!' Then the captain of the Yankee ship and the Lieutenant of the English steamer shook hands and left for the cabin, where I think -- in fact I know -- that they hobnobbed a bit before getting to business.

"'Captain,' said the English lieutenant, 'ever since we left Manila ten days ago, we have been drifting our lives away. Admiral Sir Thomas Cochrane has an idea that you are loaded with provisions. Will you help us to a port, to be repaid to you at Honolulu, as if we are pressed, we have not enough provisions to last ten days longer, while if you can help us we will shower down blessings on your head?'

"Instead of a fight, there was merry making; all hands turned to and helped stow away the provisions from the American frigate to the English ships. At the close of which the English ships saluted us, and we separated, mutually pleased with each other.

"Among the acquaintances we made that day was the owner of a distinguished name, that of the son of the famous novelist, Captain Maryatt, afterwards lost in the Mediterranean Sea." [Frederick Marryat, father of the British naval officer mentioned here is considered to be one of England's great novelists of maritime lore and adventure stories. His major works during the first half of the 19th century include *Frank Mildmay, The King's Own, Newton Foster, Peter Simple, Jacob Faithful, The Pacha of Many Tales, Japhet in Search of His Father, The Pirate and the Three Cutters, Mr. Midshipman Easy.* One of the outstanding achievements he is credited for during an illustrious career in the British Royal Navy is his compilation of a code of signals for the merchant marine which became the basis of the International Code of Signals.]

We supplied the English Squadron with a good portion of our bread stores and 400 gallons of whiskey. At 4:30, the English boats left us. We braced up the starboard tack. At 3:45, we made land ahead and hoved to. The clothes and belongings of George Fulcher were sold. The ship was pumped. Distance made is 90 miles. Latitude 14.18 north/Longitude 120.02 east.

September 10, 1845 -- The crew is employed working in the Bay of Manila. We made and reduced sail as occasion required. Lowered all the stern and quarter boats to tow the ship off the shore, it being presently one-half of a cable's length off [A cable length is 100 fathoms -- very nearly one-tenth of a nautical mile]. At 8 a.m., we took the following compass bearing; south extremity of Mari Bells Point was East Southeast, and the land at the south entrance of Manila Bay bore Southeast by East 1/2 East. The crew was inspected at quarters. Sick report has 28 men.

September 11, 1845 -- During this day, we were employed in beating up the Manila Bay. A Spanish brig and several small sail are in sight. Braced about the head yards at 9 for the purpose of paying off. Manila Bay is full of currents and we were continually getting aback or falling off before the wind. A negro named John Wright was punished as was Issac Travers with the cats for stealing knives. At 10 a.m., we came to anchor with the kedge in 24 fathoms of water. The East point of Corregidor Isle is bearing compass South Southeast and the West point is South Southwest.

Manila Bay, Island of Luzon

September 12, 1845 -- During this day, we were employed beating up to the Bay for the anchorage off the City. At 9, the crew was mustered at quarters. We made and shortened sail. Some of the men boarded the American Ship Talbot, and sent a letter bag by her to the United States. At sunset, the crew was mustered at quarters. We discovered a great current uncharted setting about the Bay in different directions. At 9:30, we came to with the starboard anchor in 7 fathoms of water. A light was bearing East by North. The spires of the Cathedral in the city lies East 3/4 North. Cabello Island is Southwest by West with a muddy bottom. The ship's draught is at aft 23 feet, 2 inches and forward 20 feet, 11 inches.

Manila Bay, Island of Luzon

September 13, 1845 -- The Spanish Captain of the fort visited the ship. We also received a visit from a French officer of the French Frigate Sabine. We saluted the Spanish Flag with 21 guns which was returned by the fort on the shore. The ship received fresh beef and vegetables for the crew. The air temperature was 86 degrees.

September 14, 1845 -- We received a load of water by lighter [a small vessel like a barge without its own means of propulsion]. Several officers visited the city. A Divine Service was performed today.

[The following extract of the Manila was given by Ship's Clerk B.F. Stevens:

"This city is the capital of the Spanish possession in the East. It is beautifully situated at the foot of a beautiful bay into which a river empties and on which the city is founded.

"Manila proper is a walled city, having its portcullises [a protective iron grating hung over the gateway of a fortress to prevent entry until it is raised] and drawbridges at every entrance, though generally speaking the country round for miles is called by that name. There are but few handsome buildings here, with the exception of the cathedrals and the Governor's house. Most of the convents are overgrown with moss and have an antiquated appearance, and maybe considered relics of a former century. Without the walls, there is a larger cigar factory belonging to the Spanish government, where all the Manila cigars are made.

"The amusements of the Spanish residents are riding, theatricals and music. At vespers every morning may be seen hundreds of 'calisas' [horse-drawn carriage] through and around the city, filled with fair occupants, and until a late hour in the evening this scene remains a gay one. It is in fact the only time the Spanish ladies are out. Every Thursday and Saturday evenings the bands perform in front of the palace, and I must confess that I never heard music played any better in my life.

"Most of the shopkeepers in Manila are Chinese, though their stores and articles are arranged upon the European plans. This class of people form quite a body and are numbered at several thousands.

September 17, 1845 -- We received 8 coils of Manila rope in the boatswain department and 2 lbs. of line. We also received another boat load of water. The crew was particularly pleased to see the new supply of 15 barrels of whiskey. The clerk reported also loading on 2 barrels of molasses, 17 bags of rice, and still another load of water.

We have had several attempts at desertion in the fourth cutter. The men who made the attempt, Peter Williams, William Valiant, and John Brown were all brought back the same day. We prepare for sea. Sick list has 43 men.

City of Manila

September 20, 1845 -- The City of Manila is situated on the southwest side of the island of Luzon or Luconia. It is said to contain about 90,000 inhabitants, most of them are Indians and half breeds. The city is built on an extensive flat and is surrounded by rice fields. The European City is on the south side of the river and is walled in with a strong wall and encompassed on every side by a ditch about 40 feet wide.

The walls have many holes and are already filled with guns. No doubt many more are stored away in the arsenals. A river about 200 yards wide runs through the town, though it has been well walled up on both sides for many miles. A beautiful and well built bridge crosses the river about one mile from its mouth. The European City is well built and its houses are usually clean. They are usually around two stories high and are built of stone or brick. The city is full of churches and some of them have a truly ancient look and are truly grand and splendid inside. A stranger would be surprised at the number of priests who meet him in the streets. Tis said that they are the smartest and most influential men in the place. They certainly are polite men and have a sort of bon-vivant look about them that speaks of things other than spiritual food. The town north of the river is not walled. It is very well built and is the business part of Manila.

The streets are quite regular. The town is cut up in two or three directions by wide canals. These were no doubt dug to facilitate commerce and also for defense. They are all crossed in many places by excellent little shops or stores in the principal streets.

The cigar manufacturers are well worth seeing. There are employed in these places over 7,000 girls. It is a beautiful sight; all are busy and still they find time to smile on a stranger or to say "Buenos dias, señor," to a young man. Some of these girls are quite beautiful and they spoke with much soft music that I for one delighted to listen to their voices.

The Manila cheroots are as good as the Havana cigars, some even prefer them to those of Cuba. For my part, I would rather smoke a cheroot made by a pretty Manila girl than the Havanas made by African negroes, even though the Havanas may be the best.

Manila Bay is surrounded by high mountains that appear to have been volcanic craters. Shocks of earthquakes are sometimes felt in Manila. The bay is quite open and almost free from danger if a shock occurs. There is good anchorage about 3 miles from the town. The bottom is very muddy though. To enter the bay does not require a pilot. Near the city there are large fields of rice. The roads are generally in fine order and the views very pretty and pleasant. Part of the Indian town is built of bamboo. The Indians appear to be very ingenious and can weave a kind of cloth from the fibers of the pineapple which is much finer than any kind of silk.

Everyone in Manila is a Christian. The Spaniards established their religion as they conquered. The sword is of great use to some natives. For it is only by the sword that they can be civilized. The sword has persuaded or converted more natives to religion than mere persuasion. But still, though these people have been converted by force, anyone can see the improvement of their country. Tis said the population has doubled itself several times since the conquest.

I have had a great number of people speak against the Catholics for their intrigues with savage natives. In this instance though, I must say that they have enslaved the country but also have enriched the country as well. I believe that the slavery of the people will break forth one day so that they will enjoy a full and perfect liberty and by being civilized they will know how to appreciate it.

There are in Manila about 3,000 troops who are mostly natives. Manila is extremely well fortified and could easy make a stout defense if stout hearts could hold it. But the Spaniards have a saying that it takes a Spaniard to build, a Frenchman to take and an Englishman to keep their forts. The ditch is nearly filled up on the south side of the town. The ruins of the wall would enable a storming party to creep in. Tis said though that a golden key would unlock all the gates of Manila.

There are two long moles [piers or breakwaters] built out into the sea. One of them is a light house. The other has a battery of long guns. On certain evenings there is a pretty event there. On the Papai, all the pretty Spanish girls can be seen about sundown there in their Valantis [a formal dress with veil]. The band of the garrison, a splendid one, usually attends. In fact, from 4 p.m. till 10 at night is the stirring time of day when everybody wishes to see and be seen.

Manila City was founded about 1640. About 15 miles above the city is a lake [Bahia] 30 miles across. It is surrounded by high mountains and bordered with Indian villages. The dress of the Indian girls is about half-savage, half-civilized. The skirts of their dresses are worn loose from the body, sometimes they slip rather low for our modest nations, etc. The men dress much like the Europeans. They wear hats, the women never wear more than a handkerchief or veil over their heads.

The Island of Luzon is about 360 miles long. It is a very rich and fertile island. Its products are mainly for export and are tobacco, hemp, cigars, sugar and rice. There are several vessels hove down in the river. They are hove down by a single purchase lashed to a derrick [a large spar rigged for hoisting boats or cargo] between the fore and main masts. The derrick was secured to a stout lashing between the fore and main masts. The main mast was well stayed aft by means of a hawser through the stern or thereabouts.

The largest ship had also two relieving tackles hooked to a belt driven down close to the water's edge. They were to ease her down or to right her if necessary. The masts were also secured by two spars lashed just below the main lashing between the fore and main mast and having the heels of the spar resting against the bulwarks. I think this is a good plan, for on the lashing between the fore and main mast, you can put as many purchases as you choose. You can make your derrick answer for a mast viz. by lashing the heel against some solid part of the ship and staying it on the off side from the hulk. A pump should be rigged in her bilge to pump her out.

September 21, 1845 -- All are now employed standing out of the bay. The ship is under fore topmast studds [studding sails are set from spars rigged out from the yards]. Also the jib and flying jib are used. At 5:20, Point Homers bore compass North 1/2 West. Monja Island bore East by South 1/4 South. Corrigidor Isle bore 3/4 South. We secured the anchor to the bows. Three men who tried to desert were punished today with one dozen each with the cats. At 9, the crew was mustered to quarters and prayers were read. Distance made these 24 hours is 64 miles. Sick report has 40 men. Latitude 15.03 north/Longitude 119.38 east.

September 24, 1845 -- The ship is under foretop mast and fore and main topgallant studding sails. We are making the best of our way for the Bashi Straits [run between the northern islands of Batan, Philippines and Taiwan]. The 4th. division exercised the small arms. At daylight, land was discovered on the weather beam. At meridian, an island is in sight one point forward of the weather bow. Some of the crew amused themselves catching several pretty little brown looking sparrow-like birds. Sick report has 37 men. Latitude 19.52 north/Longitude 121.04 east.

September 25, 1845 -- We are all employed beating up to the Bashi Isles [Batan Islands]. The Bay at Batan and Batintang Isle in sight. [Balintang channel and Batan Bay off the northern extreme of Luzon allow passage from the South China Sea in the west to the Philippine Sea in the east.]   The ship is under royals.   At meridian, Batintang Isle bore per compass East Northeast 1/4 East.   The north point of Bashi Island is Northeast 1/4 North.   The 3rd. division was exercised at the great guns and the 3rd. division of small arms was also exercised.   Distance made these 24 hours is 106 miles.   Sick report has 28 men.   Latitude 20.35 north/Longitude 124.40 east.

September 26, 1845 -- The Bashi Island is in sight to the east.   We got the larboard anchor off the bow and ready for letting go.   The 3rd. cutter was lowered and sent her with the master to find an anchorage.   At 8, we laid the main topsail to the mast.   A gun was fired and a light hoisted for the boat.   At daylight, we hoisted out all boats, stowed the gang casks in them and sent them for water.   Sails were made and reduced as situation required.

Jvana Bay, Batan Island
Bashi Group

September 27, 1845 -- We busied ourselves for most of the day watering the ship. The Bashi Islands are volcanic and are very fertile.   The scenery among them is beautiful.   They are inhabited by Indians who have been instructed in the arts, etc., by the Catholic missionaries.

The population of Batan is about 7,000.   It is only about 6 miles long and 2 miles wide.   There are several very pretty villages amongst the hills.   The town of Saint Domingo has a church and factory.   The houses of the natives are so concealed by the trees, that it would be difficult to tell where the town was and where it was not, if it were not for the steeples of the churches.

There are a great many caves in the island.   One of them is an important water supply.   We sent our men there to obtain our fresh water.   The land of these islands is very rugged and steep.   It resembles the land of Fayal and Madeira.   Tis said that shocks of earthquakes are frequent here.   About 50 miles to the south is an active volcano called Charo Babugan.   The natives appear to be very innocent and inoffensive. They did not first appear to be very innocent and inoffensive. They did not appear to be like any savages that we have seen before viz. greedy and grasping. But rather, they seemed very influenced by civilization.   We made sail at daylight having filled up with water and hoisted all the boats in.   Edward Robinson, a seaman, deserted the ship.

September 29, 1845 -- Land is still in sight to the south and west.   The 5th. division was exercised in small arms and the 1st. division was exercised at the great guns. At sunset, the crew was inspected at quarters. The anchors were secured at the bows. A heavy squall is setting in from the north and east. The ship is under royals and flying jib. Distance made these 24 hours is 50 miles. Sick list has 27 men. Latitude 19.55 north/Longitude 122.44 east.

September 30, 1845 -- Today we spliced the main brace because on this day 36 years ago, the Captain got spliced to his better half [this is a sailor's term for getting married; in this case the passage refers to Captain Percival's anniversary; usually an extra serving of rum or other refreshment was served to the crew]. The ship is under royals and flying jib. We got up all the larboard chain. The links were overhauled, washed off, and the chain locker was washed and cleaned. The 5th. Division was exercised at the great guns and the 4th. at small arms. Distance made 71 miles. Latitude 19.34 north/Longitude 123.53 east.

Pacific Ocean

October 3, 1845 -- We hoisted the first and second cutters out of the launch into the gangway in order to clean out the launch. The starboard chain was roused up and then paid below. The 3rd. Division was exercised at the great guns. We are beating to the windward but making only slow progress. A great amount of floating pumice stone was seen today. Latitude 20.53 north/Longitude 125.11 east.

October 5, 1845 -- The sailmakers are busy making a new fore topgallant sail. The crew is variously employed. The ship was also pumped out today. We have made and shortened sails to a fresh breeze as was necessary. We made a split in the jib and hauled it down. The fore topmast staysail was set. The foresail was hauled up and the fore tack was parted. We split the fore topmast, staysail, and parted the main topsail brace in two different places [common casualty report for ships in the Constitution's class, apparently the sail was torn by a storm or worn out by too much stress]. Sick report has 24 men. Latitude 22.52 north/Longitude 123.50 east.

October 9, 1845 -- The sailmakers are busily employed in making a new fore topgallant sail. The ship is now under royals and flying jib. At sunset, the crew was inspected at quarters. There is a great quantity of pumice around the ship. Some of the pieces are about the size of a 60 gallon cask. Crown Island is in sight [Miyako Jima is part of the Sakishima Archipelago in the extreme southern end of the Japanese Ryukyu chain]. Latitude 25.53 north/Longitude 126.53 east.

October 17, 1845 -- We unbent the split fore topsail and bent another. The 4th Division was exercised at the great guns. The 5th. Division exercised with the small arms and muskets. We still have a large amount of pumice around the ship. There are several albatross following along with us. Distance made 166 miles. Latitude 31.20 north/Longitude 138.35 east.

October 20, 1845 -- We are experiencing fresh gales and squally weather. Fatsisio Island in sight ahead [one of the Ogasawara chain marking the eastern boundary of the Fallopian Sea and the Pacific Ocean, south of Japan]. We had to reduce sail and double reef fore and main topsails. Split the main spencer. We are having very heavy seas. The ship is very wet. The gun deck is leaking and there is leaking in the waterways. However, the ship is riding rather well for the conditions of a heavy sea. So much pumice it appears to be a reef. Latitude 33.15 north/Longitude 143.48 east.

October 22, 1845 -- The weather is still squally as we experience very heavy seas. We have had the companionship of a large backfin whale for the last several hours. The ship is still leaking but we have managed to keep the pump at work.

Took in the topgallant sails. At 4 p.m., the weather is blowing very hard with a very heavy sea on. Took a third reef in the topsails. We furled the mizzen, and lowered the spanker. The foresail has been reefed. Set up the starboard main rigging and topmast back stays. The ship is as easy as an old shoe. Distance made is 129 miles. Sick report has 23 men. Latitude 33.40 north/Longitude 149 east.

October 25, 1845 -- We have passed great quantities of pumice stone and a lot of drift wood. This pumice is arranged in long lines running near north and south and we have frequently observed and recorded large amounts of seawood and driftwood in similar lines of direction. Distance made 130 miles. Latitude 34.31 north/Longitude 158 east.

October 31, 1845 -- The ship is under topgallant sails and jib. We unbent the main top gallant sail and bent another in its place. We parted the main top gallant sheet, split the sail and furled it. We split the job, unbent it and bent another one. The ship was also pumped today. Distance made is 166 miles. Whole distance run is 29,385 miles. Latitude 33.08 north/Longitude 173.11 east.

November 4, 1845 -- During this day, we have experienced the most violent sea. There are terrific squalls and very high seas all around us. At 5 p.m., we were struck by a particularly heavy squall that parted the fore sheets. The storm also sprung the fore yard and slightly carried away the fore clew garnets, somehow or other hooked the clew jigger -- don't know how nor cannot find out. We hauled up the foresail and furled. We reefed the fore and main top sails. At 8, the main topsail blew out of the bolt ropes. The storm carried away all the running rigging except the weather reef

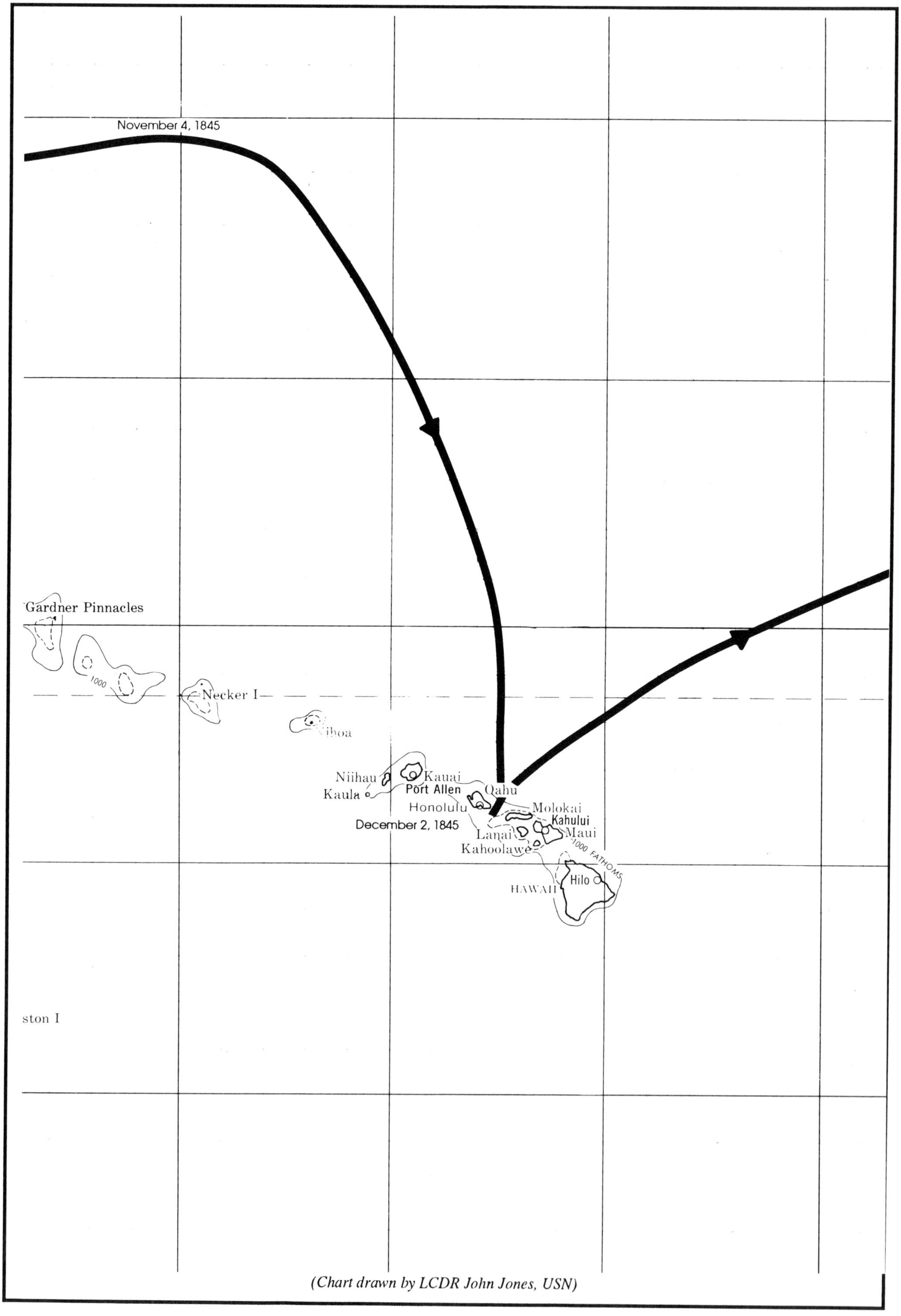

November 4, 1845

Gardner Pinnacles

1000

Necker I

Nihoa

Niihau   Kauai
Kaula   Port Allen   Qahu
         Honolulu   Molokai
December 2, 1845   Kahului
                    Lanai   Maui
                 Kahoolawe
                              1000 FATHOMS
                    HAWAII   Hilo

ston I

(Chart drawn by LCDR John Jones, USN)

tackle. We bent down the top gallant studding sail. The forward halyards went past the end abaft and thus spilled. We hauled up the remnants of the sail and furled it. Distance made 221 miles. Latitude 34.42 north/Longitude 165.55 west.

November 7, 1845 -- The ship is now under all plain sail. At sunset and at 9 a.m., the crew was mustered to quarters. The 4th. Division was exercised at the great guns and the 3rd. Division was exercised at the small arms. At 4:30 a.m., Charles G. Clyde, marine, departed this life. The ship is under top mast studding sail during the latter part of the day. Distance made 122 miles. Latitude by observation/Longitude by chronometer.

November 8, 1845 -- At 2 p.m., all hands were called to bury the dead and we committed the body of Charles G. Clyde to the deep. The ship is on a wind under all plain sail. The sailmakers are employed in making a new main topgallant sail. We fired 134 rounds from the great guns. This is much more than is normally done. Latitude by observation/Longitude by chronometer.

Off Oahu [Hawaiian Islands]

November 16, 1845 -- At 5:30 p.m., we discovered the Island of Marci 2 points on the larboard bow. We bent the larboard chain. The sail was reduced to the royals. At 10:30, we single reefed the fore and main topsails and double reefed the mizzen sail. The spanker was single reefed and at 12, hoved to with the main topsail to the mast.

At daylight, we made the Island of Oahu. We made sail on the larboard tack. At 10:30, we clewed up again and came to off Honolulu in 25 fathoms of water. We had a muddy bottom. Diamond Point bore compass East Southeast 3/4 East. We spotted a large church North Northeast. Veered to 68 fathoms.

Off Honolulu

November 17, 1845 -- We sent down top gallant and royal yards. The ship saluted the Hawaiian Flag with 21 guns. This salute was returned by the fort on shore. We received fresh provisions for the crew and hoisted the 1st. and 2nd. cutter in charge of the Master to obtain fresh water.

We saluted Mr. Abel, the American Consul, with 9 guns and also saluted General Miller, H.B.M., British Consul with 9 guns with the English Flag at the fore. All our boats are busily employed watering the ship. Ten of the men had to be punished for drunkenness and disobedience while working on the boats. We have also received a visit from the U.S. Commissioner Brown. We saluted him with 13 guns. The painters are busy with the outside of the ship. Samuel Chichester and Henry Shaw were shipped (given new assignments to other commands or vessels).

[On November 16, 1845, the following report was made by Ship's Clerk B.F. Stevens:

"It being Sunday when we arrived, we found everything as still and quiet as could be -- not a boat was seen in the harbor and every whaleship appeared possessed with the spirit of quietness. During our stay I had many opportunities of visiting the town, though I can not say that I was much pleased with its appearance. It is about the size of South Boston -- does not contain any beautiful buildings, though the scenery around it is very grand. Were it not for this latter the place would be unworthy of note.

"It is the great depot of the Pacific for whalers to refresh and repair in -- in fact, were it not for this portion of commerce of the world, but little good would result to Oahu and the other islands of the group.

"There are about twenty-three American families residing here, besides a few English and French, and the business is entirely in the hands of foreign residents; in fact, the councillors and advisors of the King are selected from this class of the people, many of whom have taken the oath of allegiance to the Hawaiian Government.

"There are six of these islands altogether of one government, two of which, besides Oahu, viz. Owyhu and Mowee, are becoming of importance for the advantage they offer to those who are engaged in the whale fishery. Besides this they are the stopping place of many vessels crossing the Pacific to the East Indies, though the present policy of the merchants with regard to prices is calculated to render them gradually of less importance. The most common article of American manufacture cannot be purchased here unless at an advance of from 1 to 200 per cent on the cost. The duty upon each article is but 5 or 10 per cent.

"Most people traveling and who are desirous of purchasing clothing cheap look to the Sandwich Islands, where our countrymen reside, to enable them to lay out their money to the best advantage. Many of them did so, but alas! in buying only necessary articles we were satisfied of the great imposition practiced.

"With regard to the people, in consequence of the severe laws enacted through the instrumentality of foreign missionaries and those who have lately become subjects of his Majesty, they are gradually decreasing in number and will in a few short years be entirely swept away. From what I have observed and learned from others, I judge their condition to be far worse now than it was thirty years since, when Christians had not secured a foothold among them.

"They appear mild and well disposed, though I am informed they are extremely indolent; perhaps much of this latter is caused by the circumstance that much of their labor would be devoted, under the present system, to the Kings and Chiefs. Again, they see foreigners purchasing lands around them and inch by inch taking from them the soil upon which God in His Mercy placed them. So far has this latter been carried that many natives have petitioned the King not to permit any foreigners to buy any land, and have even asked that he will put away his foreign advisers.

"Between the foreign residents generally and the missionaries, who are backed by the council of the King, a hostility exists as regards the policy pursued by the latter in Christianizing and civilizing these poor natives. Of late years the conduct of the missionaries regarding their treatment of the Catholics has met with much animadversion, and I should judge that it was well deserved.

"Sending fanatics to a far country in the midst of a native race like this is not the way to make Christians of them. Had they introduced industry, energy and enterprise among the natives, these islands would have become ere this a perfect paradise, but instead they went with the Bible in one hand and a rod in the other.

"At Honolulu we received orders to repair with the least possible delay to the Mexican Coast in anticipation of a war with that power. We began an extensive load of supplies, stores, and provisions."]

[Thomas journal continues:]

December 2, 1845 -- We are standing off in Honolulu Bay. At 4:30, we discharged the pilot and filled away. Beat to quarters and loaded the guns. The anchors were secured. At 6 p.m., the east point of Oahu Isle bore compass North Northeast and Diamond Point bore nearly North.

At 10 p.m., we tacked the ship to the south and the east. At 9 went to quarters. Rove new main sheets [passing small lengths of line through the eyelet holes at the head of a sail to attach it to a yard]. At noon, the extremities of Oahu Isle bore compass South Southeast and Southwest by West 1/2 West. The ship was pumped. Our destination is Monterey, California, where we are to join the American Squadron. Latitude 21.50 north/Longitude 157.47 east.

At Sea

December 4, 1845 -- We turned the reefs out of the topsails and spanker. There is still land in sight to the north and west. At 6, we tacked the ship to the south and east. The ship is now under royals and flying jib. Distance made 91 miles. Sick report has 32 men. Latitude 23.07 north/Longitude 158.52 east.

December 7, 1845 -- The ship is under plain sail. We are making the best of our way to the north and west. The crew was mustered to quarters at sunset and at 9 a.m. At 10, the Captain read the Articles of War and also an Act of Congress relative to boys and seaman. The ship was pumped. Distance made 108 miles. Sick report 30 men. Latitude 27.44 north/Longitude 160.14 west.

January 6 and 7, 1846 -- The ship is under studding sails. We can see the Island of Guadaloupe at North and East. By 8 a.m., the east end of Guadaloupe [Mexican island off the Pacific coast of the Baja peninsula] bore per compass North Northwest and the went end bore Northwest 3/4 North. We saw several whales today in quite a large quantity. Two men were punished today for fighting. Sick report 42 men. Latitude 26.09 north/Longitude 115.15 west.

January 8, 1846 -- Our gun crews have been conducting an experiment with the flannel, felt and rubber cylinders. They have found that Indian rubber cylinders always stuck fast to the bottom of the gun. The flannel and felt were better, and it is probable that the felt was the best. But, there was but little difference between the flannel and felt. We got a cast of lead 60 fathoms deep today and found no bottom. Latitude 24.33 north/Longitude 113.46 west.

January 9, 1846 -- We got a cast of lead 100 fathoms and still found no bottom. There is land in sight to the east. The ship is under larboard studding sail part of the day. The 4th. Division practiced with the small arms while the 1st. Division practiced with the great guns. There are several whales in sight and also a great number of sea birds. [Latitude and longitude are not included in this entry.]

January 10, 1846 -- At 3 p.m., we set all the larboard studding sails. At 7 a.m., we took them in and braced up on the larboard tack. At sunset we can make out a sail on the larboard beam. There is land in sight to the east. The boatswain and gang are employed rigging a purchase [tackle, windlass, capstan and screw or handspike to move heavy equipment or extend the ship's rigging] to get the patent anchor out of the forecastle and onto the bow. Latitude 23.15 north/Longitude 111.24 west.

January 11, 1846 -- Ship under all larboard sails. We got the anchor over the side. Land in sight on the larboard bow. At daylight, there are two sails in sight. They

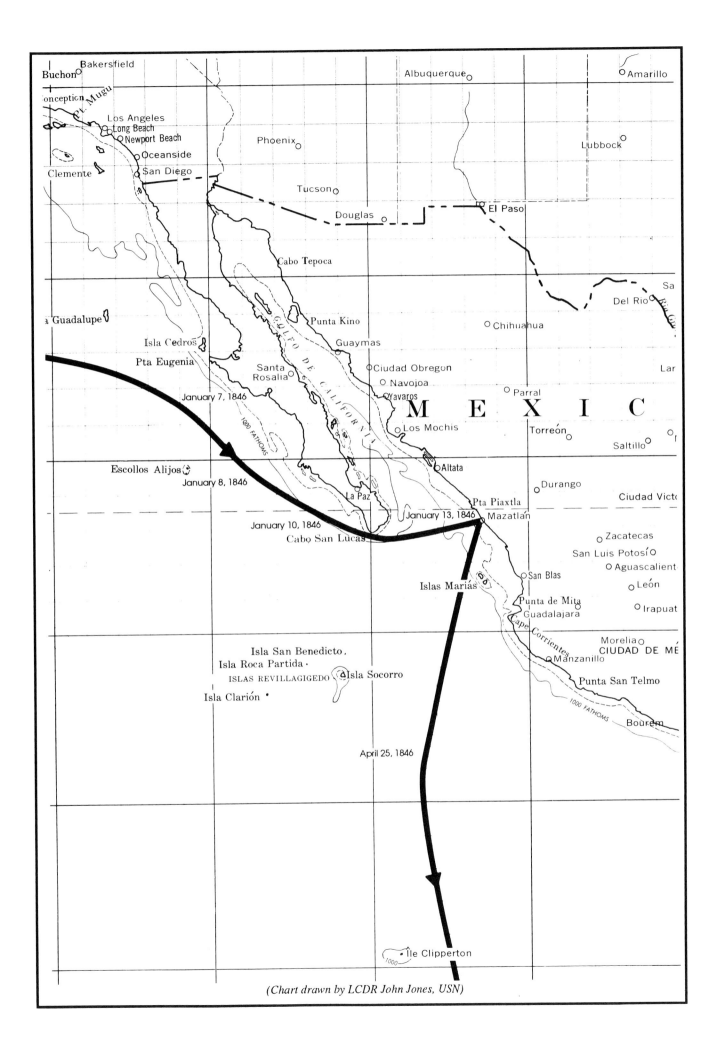

Buchon

Bakersfield

Albuquerque

Amarillo

Pt. Mugu

Conception

Los Angeles
Long Beach
Newport Beach

Phoenix

Lubbock

Clemente

Oceanside

San Diego

Tucson

Douglas

El Paso

Cabo Tepoca

Sa

Del Rio

Rio G

Guadalupe

Punta Kino

Chihuahua

Isla Cedros

GULFO DE CALIFORNIA

Guaymas

Pta Eugenia

Santa
Rosalia

Ciudad Obregon

Navojoa

Lar

January 7, 1846

Yavaros

M E X I C

1000 FATHOMS

Los Mochis

Torreón

Escollos Alijos

January 8, 1846

Altata

Parral

Saltillo

Durango

Ciudad Victo

La Paz

January 10, 1846

Pta Piaxtla

January 13, 1846

Mazatlán

Cabo San Lucas

Zacatecas

San Luis Potosí

Aguascalient

San Blas

León

Islas Mariás

Punta de Mita

Irapuat

Guadalajara

Cape Corrientes

Isla San Benedicto.

Morelia
CIUDAD DE MÉ

Isla Roca Partida.

Manzanillo

ISLAS REVILLAGIGEDO

Isla Socorro

Punta San Telmo

Isla Clarión

1000 FATHOMS

Bourem

April 25, 1846

Ile Clipperton

1000

(Chart drawn by LCDR John Jones, USN)

seem to be under American colors. They are just under Cape Saint Lucas [Cape Saint Lucas is at the extreme southern end of the Baja peninsula]. We showed our colors in return. At 10 a.m., all hands called to muster. (No Latitude or Longitude for this entry)

January 12, 1846 -- We sent a boat over to inspect the vessels at anchor under Cape Saint Lucas. At dark, we burnt a blue light and fired a gun. The boat returned and informed the Captain that they were the whale ship Saint Laurina out of Sag Harbour. Several men were punished today. One was caught gambling and the other two were fighting. [No Latitude or Longitude for this entry].

Off Mazatlan, Mexico [principal Mexican port on the mainland, southern end of the Gulf of California].

January 13, 1846 -- The ship is under starboard studding sails. A sail is in sight to the west. There are a number of whales and other large fish in sight. We also can make a sail to the north. Land is on the starboard bow.

Mazatlan Bay, Mexico

The weather is very squally as we discovered the American Squadron at anchor in Mazatlan Bay. We double reefed the topsails and single reefed the spanker. At 10, we sounded in 51 fathoms water and found a soft and muddy bottom. At 6:30, we furled the mainsail. At 7:30, the ship was tacked to the south and west. Land in sight and bearing East 1/2 North. We saluted the Broad Pendant of Commodore John D. Sloat, Commander of the squadron, with 9 guns. Distance in miles per log is 38,207 miles.

January 15, 1846 -- We are standing in for the anchorage of Mazatlan. During this day, we have remarkably good weather. At 1:40, we clewed up and came to with the larboard anchor in 10 fathoms. The sails were then furled. Took the following compass bearings: Rock-South by East, Castilla -- Northwest by North, Everton -- West 1/4 South. We veered to with the chain in 34 fathoms. The ship was next moored with 43 fathoms on the starboard and 53 fathoms on the larboard.

January 16, 1846 -- The ships Savannah, Levant and Plymouth were at anchor along with 10 other men-of-war of different classes. There were also several British vessels there including the America and Frolic. The Levant signalled us of a court-martial proceeding. [When war commenced with Mexico, Commodore Sloat was placed in command of U.S. naval forces at Mazatlan, which consisted of 13 vessels from various classes. USS *Constitution* joined this squadron. They were under orders to act in concert with General Zachary Taylor, then in command of the land forces.]

January 23, 1846 -- Today, we half-masted the colors in mourning for the death of Ex-President Andrew Jackson. On the 24th., we fired minute guns. We are busy securing provisions for our voyage home. Since have been at anchor, we have had to punish so many of the crew for drunkenness. Many are employed caulking the ship and there is painting as well. On the 26th., an English brig drifted foul of us and stove the gig. We hoisted her in for repairs. Still a great deal of caulking to be done.

April 23, 1846 -- At 3:00 p.m., we fired a gun and showed the cornet. We next called all hands to up the anchor for "Home." Got underway all plain sail. We hove to with the main topsail to the mast. Captain Percival let the ship fill away and we are standing off and on the anchorage of Mazatlan. Gave our departing signals and the Captain ordered a salute of 13 guns. The Commodore answered the salute with 9 guns. Unbent the sheet and chain cables.

April 25, 1846 -- Today, we saw a partial eclipse of the sun. At 9 a.m., the crew was inspected at quarters. The Boatswain is employed overhauling the rigging. The ship is now at sunset under all starboard studding sail. Distance made 130 miles. Latitude 16.33 north/Longitude 108.21 west.

[Ship's Clerk B.F. Stevens described the feelings aboard ship as they turned for home:

"The day we left Mexico for home, General Taylor, I think, fought the Battle of El Molino del Rey, or King's Mills. You may be sure there was no looking back as we wended our way out of the harbor of Mazatlan, where we had left our brother tars to remain, no one knew how long, before orders would come to them to start for home; but when we did a backward glance we were too far away to be discerned with the most powerful of glasses. Our main deck was a scene of jollity till late that night, for there was a brilliant moon the night of the Battle of El Molino del Rey, although we knew not that it had been fought till afterwards.

"And our crew, who had not been home since November, 1843, made the 'welkin ring' [celebration of various kinds including songs, toasts, dancing and scrimshaws from shells and other materials as gifts for loved ones upon arrival home] that first night of their homeward trip, and the old toast of 'Sweethearts and Wives' echoed from the lips of as stalwart a crew as ever trod the deck of an American man-of-war on their return to their native land and the home of their adoption.

"And there were many good voices, too, in that hardy crew which tolled out the old and new sea songs of every sort and fashion, particularly that beautiful ditty, 'As we sailed along the lowlands, lowlands, low, as we sailed along the lowlands, low.' And so we wended our course southerly towards the famous old Spanish city, Valparaiso, the great commercial port of Chile."]

May 5, 1846 -- We are experiencing the most hot and unpleasant weather, but tis no matter as we are homeward bound. It could be twice as hot. Old Whit is on the gun deck making a new foresail. In rainy weather, he and his gang block up the gun deck and in fair weather, they occupy the lee side of the quarter deck so there is no chance for a reefer either in fair or foul weather. However, he has not thrown his time away, for there has been made by him a new suit of sails for this ship. We discovered and charted a current of 6 fathoms per hour. Distance made 47 miles. Sick report 32 men. Latitude 4.08 north/Longitude 106.01 west.

May 21, 1846 -- During this day we have had winds varying from the south and to the west and then to the east. It is clear and pleasant. At 4:40 p.m., the crew was inspected at quarters. The ship was pumped out. At 1:55, we took in all studding sails and braced sharp up. At 7:20, we tacked to the south and east. John Chippey was punished with one dozen lashes of the cat for insolence to the Boatswain. The 1st. Division was exercised at the great guns and the 2nd. Division with the small arms and muskets. The carpenters are employed repairing the combings of the main hatch. Distance made 92 1/2 miles. Sick report 32 men. [No latitude or longitude citings given for this entry.]

May 22, 1846 -- Today we fitted a pair of main topmast backstays. After we got them up, we sent down a pair of old ones. The sailmakers are employed on a new foresail and busy repairing the old sails. At 4:40, the crew was inspected at quarters. The ship was pumped out once again. At 11:55 p.m., a light air sprung up so we set the mainsail and spanker. At 8:50 a.m., we tacked to the south and the west. At 9 a.m., we exercised the crew at quarters. We fired from the gun and spar deck divisions 36 shot. The guns were double shotted for the purpose of experimenting on the breechings. It carried away two of the breechings of the spar deck guns. Distance made 22 miles. [No latitude or longitude citings given for this entry.]

May 27, 1846 -- At 2 p.m., we took in all the studding sails and braced around on the starboard tack. At 4:00, the crew was inspected at quarters. The ship was pumped out. At 5:30, we braced around to the larboard tack. At 7, we set the larboard studding sails and hauled down the head sails. At 3:30, we beat to quarters

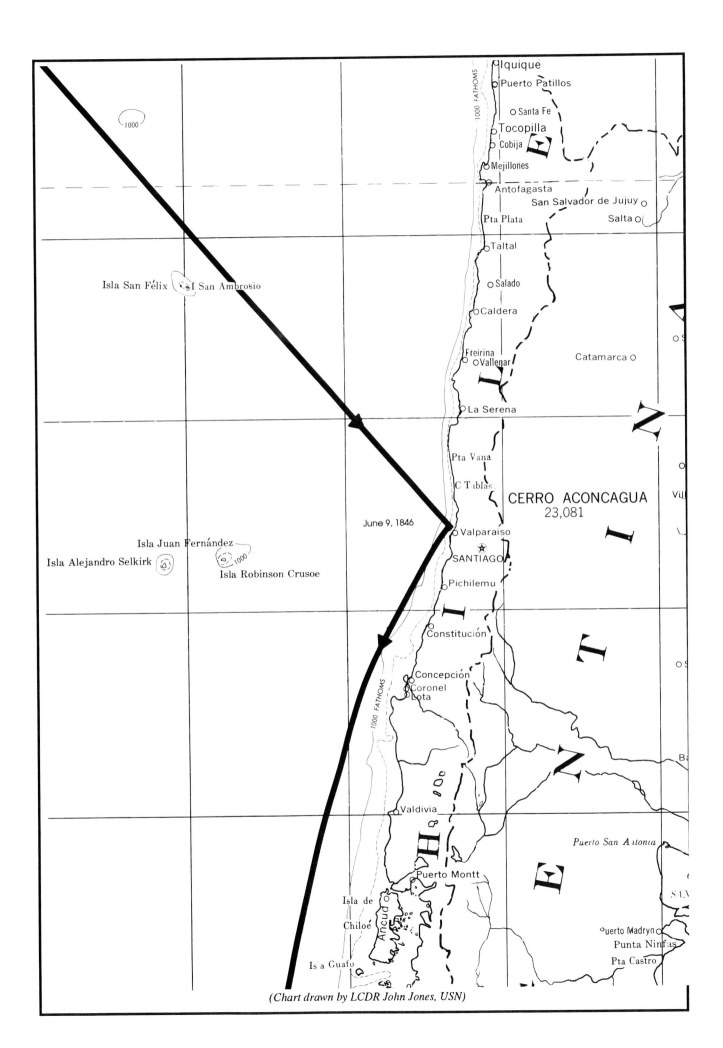

Iquique
Puerto Patillos
Santa Fe
Tocopilla
Cobija
Mejillones
Antofagasta
San Salvador de Jujuy
Salta
Pta Plata
Taltal
Salado
Caldera
Freirina
Vallenar
Catamarca
La Serena
Pta Vana
C T iblas
CERRO ACONCAGUA
23,081
Vil
June 9, 1846
Valparaiso
SANTIAGO
Isla Juan Fernández
Isla Alejandro Selkirk
Isla Robinson Crusoe
Pichilemu
Isla San Félix
I San Ambrosio
1000
1000 FATHOMS
Constitución
Concepción
Coronel
Lota
1000 FATHOMS
Valdivia
Puerto San A itonia
B
E
Isla de
Chiloé
Puerto Montt
Ancud
ouerto Madryn
Is a Guato
Punta Ninfas
Pta Castro

(Chart drawn by LCDR John Jones, USN)

and cleared the ship ready for action. At 4:05 a.m., we secured the larboard guns and beat a retreat. At 9, inspected the quarters. Exercised the 4th. Division at the great guns. Distance made 95 1/2 miles. Sick report 30 men. [No latitude or longitude citings given for this entry.]

June 9, 1846 -- At 3:50 p.m., we showed our colors to a brig on the weather bow. At 4:10 p.m., the brig showed Chilean colors. At 4:40 p.m., the crew was inspected at quarters. We ran out the main deck guns. The ship was also pumped. At 6 a.m., William Wallace and John Tyrer were punished with six lashes of the colt for skulking. There are two sail in sight. At 9 a.m., the crew was inspected at quarters. The 2nd. and 5th. Divisions were exercised at the great guns. At 11:20 a.m., a sail was reported from the fore topmast head two points on the bow. At meridian the two sail to the north were out of sight. We are carrying studding sails larboard and starboard alternately. Sick report 31 men. [No latitude or longitude citings given for this entry.]

Valparaiso, Chile

June 14, 1846 -- Commences with light breezes from the south and the east and clear pleasant weather. In the middle watch [midnight to 4 a.m.] the wind was from the south and north. In the watch from 4 to 8 a.m., the wind was from the south and east. We sent down the topgallant yards. Housed the main and mizzen and sent down the fore topgallant masts. Roused [pulled together on a cable or hawser without the assistance of a capstan or windlass] in 1 and 1/2 fathoms on the larboard chain. We got the fore topsail yard into the top. Sent out a boat. The kedge and hawser were sent out astern.

The American Consul Dorr visited the ship and on leaving we saluted him with nine guns. We boarded the H.B.M. Frigate Grampas under Captain Morton. She is 100 days from England. We received fresh beef and vegetables for the crew. There are three sail in the offing. At 9:30, the crew was inspected at quarters. At 10 a.m., all hands were called to muster and we had divine service performed by the Reverend Mr. Trumbull. John Haley was regularly discharged from the sea service of the United States. At meridian, we fired a salute of 21 guns with the Chilean colors at the mizzen which was returned by the same number from the Fort on the shore.

June 20, 1846 -- We have had a great problem with violations on the liberty leave. The 1st. cutter has been sent to fill the water tanks. At 3 p.m., the American "Charge de Affaires" visited the ship. He was given a 17 gun salute. We received a lighter [barge] alongside loaded with wood.

Several of the men who were not American citizens have requested discharge and it is usually granted one being John J. Bower. They are sent to shore with the lighter. William Hayle served onboard as a supervisor for the American Consul. After the men mustered at quarters it was found that the following men were missing: Charles H. Prince, Thomas Prott, Robert Keys, Joseph Welsh, Joseph Riley, Charles Seymour, John Collins, and John Hopson.

At 10, all hands were called to up anchor. We got up the starboard anchor and hove the ship ahead by a line to the British steamer Sampson. The French and English men of war in the port sent their boats to tow us and took the ship in tow. At 11:30, we hoisted the jib and flying jib and cast off the foreign boats. At meridian, we set the spanker as our own boats were towing us out.

June 24, 1846 -- At 3:00 p.m., we sent down the mizzen royal yard and unbent the sail. At 3:15, we furled the mizzen top gallant sail. At 3:40, we took two reefs in the mizzen topsail. The sailmakers are busily engaged repairing a mainsail. At 4:30 p.m., the crew was inspected at quarters. The ship was pumped out.

The middle part of the day, we experienced moderate winds and fresh breezes. There have been some light squalls. We made and reduced sail as to suit the weather. The day ends with light winds and cloudy weather with drizzly rain. We are making all sails carrying starboard studding sails. At 9 a.m., the crew was inspected at quarters. At 9:10, all hands were called to witness the punishments inflicted with one dozen lashes on each for various offenses. At 11:50 a.m., Henry Mathews departed this life. Distance made 174 1/4 miles.

June 28, 1846 -- At 1 p.m., we reduced sail to fore and main top gallant sail. We double reefed the jib, while the mizzen topsail was also double reefed and a single reef was taken in the spanker. At 4 p.m., we set the fore top mast staysail. At 4:40, all hands were called to take a single reef in the fore and main topsail and furled the topgallant sails. The ship was pumped out, this has almost become a daily activity. The middle part of the day we have had moderate breezes these 24 hours. At 10:30 p.m., we set the fore and main top gallant sails. At 1:30, set the fore and main top gallant sails. At 1:30, set fore topmast studding sail and mizzen top gallant sail. The day ends with fresh breezes and cloudy weather. Distance made 198 1/2 miles. [No latitude or longitude citings given for this entry.]

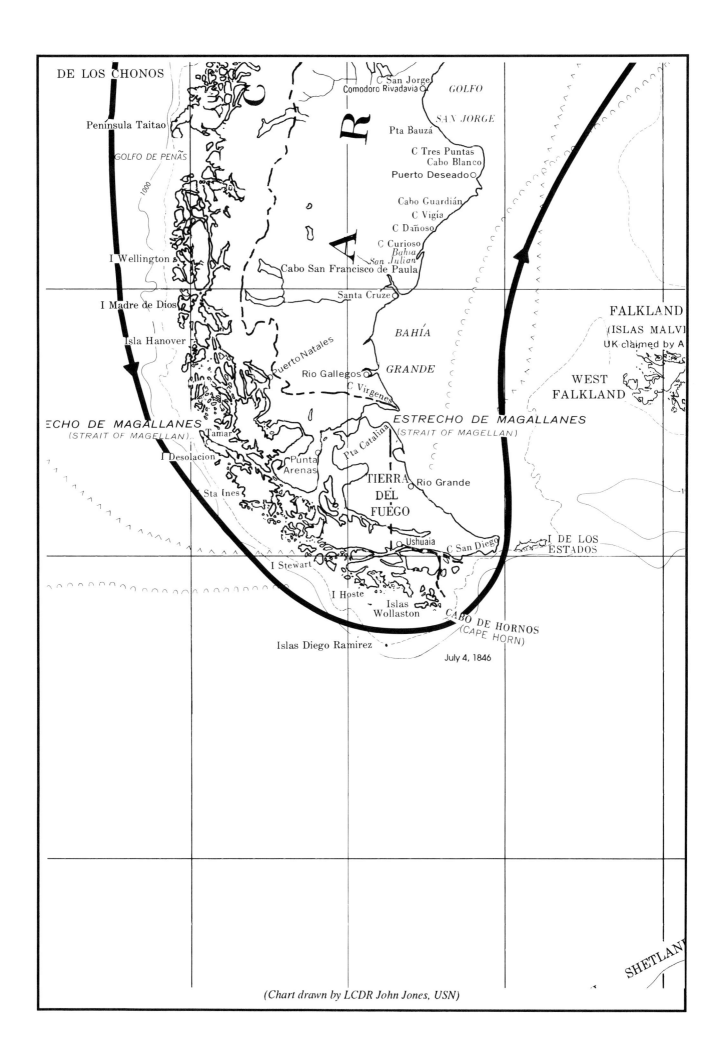

DE LOS CHONOS

Península Taitao

GOLFO DE PEÑAS

1000

I Wellington

I Madre de Dios

Isla Hanover

ECHO DE MAGALLANES
(STRAIT OF MAGELLAN)

I Desolacion

Sta Ines

I Stewart

I Hoste

Islas
Wollaston

Islas Diego Ramirez

C San Jorge
Comodoro Rivadavia

GOLFO

SAN JORGE

Pta Bauzá

C Tres Puntas
Cabo Blanco
Puerto Deseado

Cabo Guardián
C Vigía
C Dañoso
C Curioso
Bahía
San Julián
Cabo San Francisco de Paula

Santa Cruz

BAHÍA

GRANDE

Puerto Natales

Rio Gallegos
C Virgenes

ESTRECHO DE MAGALLANES
(STRAIT OF MAGELLAN)

Tamar

Pta Catalina

Punta
Arenas

TIERRA
DEL
FUEGO

Rio Grande

Ushuaia
C San Diego

I DE LOS
ESTADOS

CABO DE HORNOS
(CAPE HORN)

July 4, 1846

FALKLAND
(ISLAS MALVI
UK claimed by A

WEST
FALKLAND

SHETLAN

(Chart drawn by LCDR John Jones, USN)

July 1, 1846 -- At 4:00 p.m., we passed through a very heavy squall. The main royals, flying jib and topgallant sails were furled. We took a single reef in the mizzen topsails as soon as the squall was over.

The fore and main top gallant sail were set again. At 4:30 p.m., we single reefed the fore and main topsails. At 5:30, a double reef was taken in the fore mizzen topsails. The main royal yard was sent down. At 6:30, we hauled down and stowed the jib and furled the spanker. At 7, we close reefed the mizzen topsail.

The middle part of these twenty four hours brought very unsettled weather. At 2 a.m., we wore the ship to the south and west. The main sail was furled and took in fore and main topsails and set down the spencer. At 7 a.m., we wore the ship to the south and east. At 7:30 a.m., we turned one reef out of the topsails and set the mainsails. The ship was pumped out. The day ends with still more squalls to come. Michael McLaughlin was punished with one dozen lashes of the cat for skulking. Distance made 135 miles.

Cape Horn

[Ship's Clerk B.F. Stevens described the rounding of Cape Horn on July 4, 1846:

"We rounded it in a driving snowstorm. We soon passed into the South Atlantic Ocean and made for Rio de Janeiro, which we had left more than two years before for Madagascar in company with the French man-of-war sloop Berceau, which was fated to be wrecked on the wild coast of that island, after "Old Ironsides" had reached her home in safety. Not one soul was saved from the Berceau, while but twenty-seven of our crew passed over the boarderland. Strange is the lot of those 'who go down to the seas in ships'. We can at least spare a tear to the memory of those with whom we sailed in company across an ocean of thousands of miles, whom we met at Zanzibar and Madagascar, but now whose bones are whitening at the bottom of the ocean, while we had sailed in security and returned home in joy to our dear ones."]

July 15, 1846 -- At 3, we discovered a sail on the weather beam standing to the south. At 4:40, the royal yards were sent down. At 5, all hands were called to single reef the topsails. The topgallant sail was also taken in. At 6:30, we wore the ship.

A French barque was spotted at 8 a.m. We showed our colors to her. She was off our larboard bow. At 9, we shortened the sail and hove to with the main topsail. We spoke to her and communicated to her our position. She informed us that there was immediate need for a surgeon.

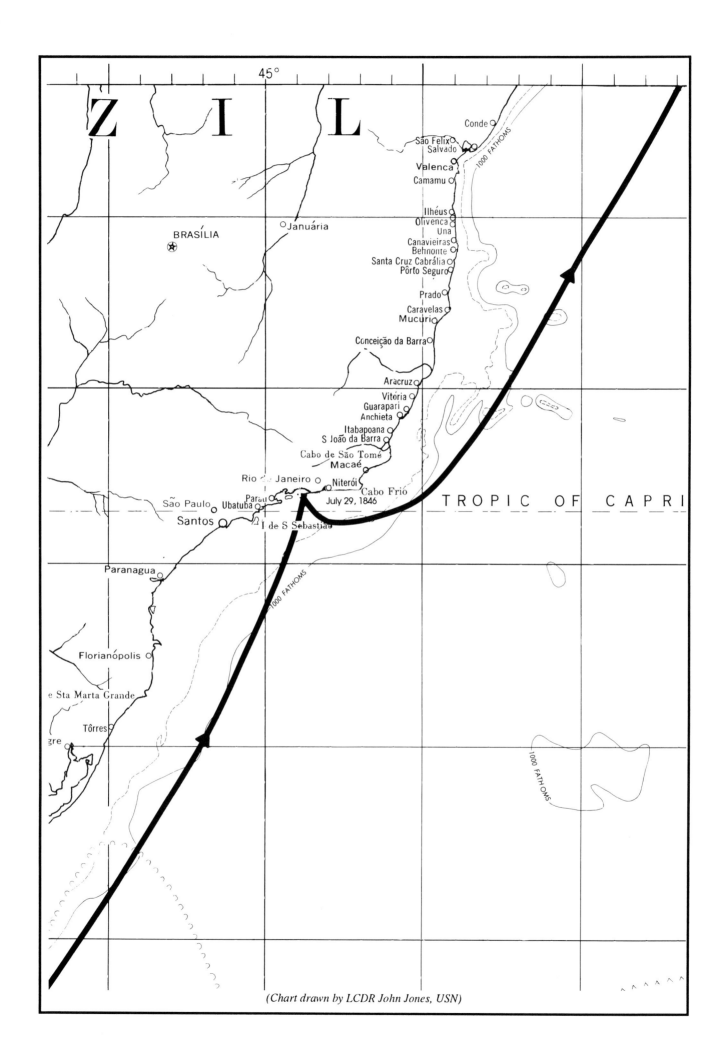

ZIL

Conde

São Felix
Salvado
Valença
Camamu

Ilhéus
Olivença
Una
Canavieiras
Belmonte
Santa Cruz Cabrália
Pôrto Seguro

Prado

Caravelas
Mucuri

Conceição da Barra

BRASÍLIA
○ Januária

Aracruz

Vitória
Guarapari
Anchieta

Itabapoana
S João da Barra
Cabo de São Tomé
Macaé

Rio de Janeiro
Niterói
Cabo Frio
July 29, 1846

São Paulo   Paraty
Ubatuba

Santos   I de S Sebastião

T R O P I C   O F   C A P R I

Paranagua

1000 FATHOMS

Florianópolis

e Sta Marta Grande

Tôrres

gre

1000 FATHOMS

1000 FATHOMS

(Chart drawn by LCDR John Jones, USN)

We sent our surgeon over to them at the request of the Master of the French vessel. At 10, Surgeon D.D. McLeod and a French seaman by the name of Peter Mace returned to our vessel. The Frenchman had broken his leg. We found out that he belonged to the French Barque Juste of St. Malo and was bound for Mazatlan when the accident occurred. We soon filled away and made all sail with the wind on our larboard quarter. The Frenchman would be our passenger as far as Rio. Distance made 90 1/2 miles. [No latitude or longitude citings given for this entry.]

July 20, 1846 -- Today, we have had a terrible tragedy onboard ship. While hauling out the weather main jigger, the strap of the leading block struck John Moore, seaman, in the head and fractured his skull. Distance made 94 miles. Latitude 33.31 south/Longitude 49.00 west.

July 27, 1846 -- At 2:30 p.m., we discovered a sail on the larboard bow standing to the south and west. At 4:31, the ship was pumped out. At daylight, land was sighted two points on the larboard bow. We then began standing in for Rio de Janeiro. At meridian, the light house on Razor Island bore per compass North Northeast and ahead and in sight at a distance of 12 miles. Distance made 153 3/4 miles. Latitude 23.15 south/Longitude 43.15 west.

Harbor of Rio de Janeiro [Brazil]

July 29, 1846 -- We stood in for the anchorage at 2:40 p.m. As we hoisted our numbers [signal pennants], we were answered by the American squadron.

At 3 p.m., we fired a salute of 13 guns which was answered by the U.S. Flagship Columbia under the command of Commandant Rosseau with 11 guns.

At 3:30, we clewed up and came to with the larboard anchor in 13 fathoms. The sails were furled and the ship moored with 55 fathoms on the larboard anchor and 40 fathoms on the starboard. At 4 p.m., a Brazilian flag at the fore saluted us with 21 guns which was also answered by 21 guns from the fort on shore. At sunset, we sent down the top gallant and royal yards. At daylight, we exchanged numbers with the U.S. Brig Bainbridge at anchor. Received a good supply of fresh beef and vegetables for the crew. The 1st. and 2nd. cutters were hoisted out. At 10 a.m., the U.S. Consul, our former passenger, Mr. Henry A. Wise, visited the ship. We saluted him with 9 guns. At meridian, we fired a salute of 21 guns in honor of the French Revolution.

July 30, 1846 -- Today we received onboard 140 gallons of water from a water tank. The painters are employed in painting the ship outside. At 6:30 p.m., we fired

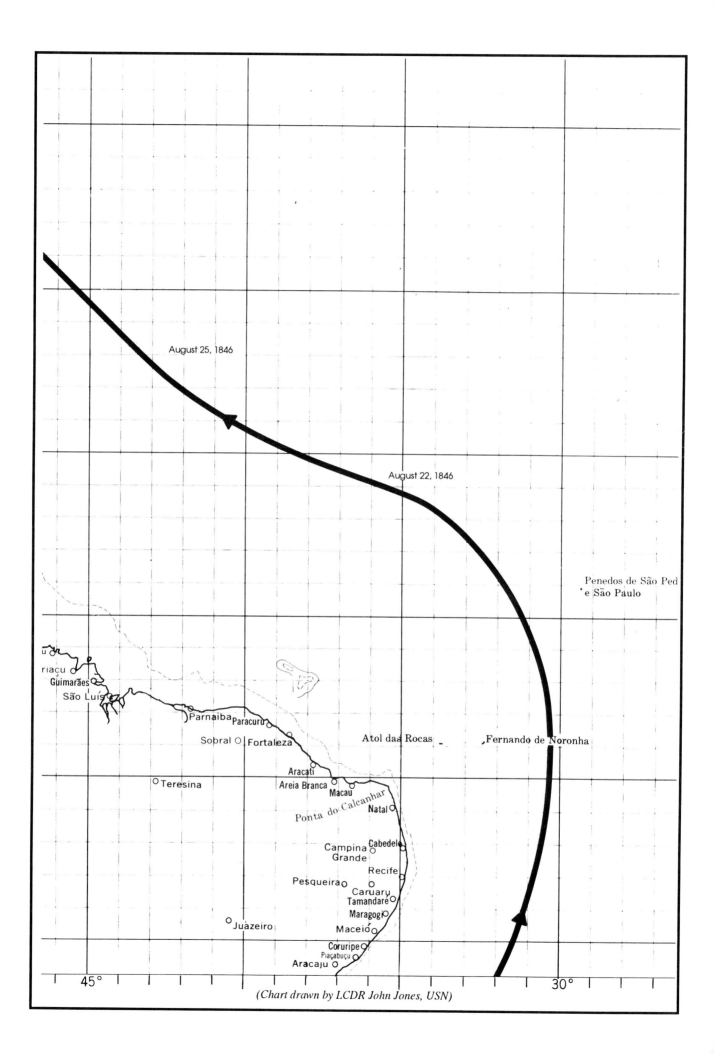

August 25, 1846

August 22, 1846

Penedos de São Ped
e São Paulo

u
riaçu
Guimarães
São Luís
Parnaiba
Paracuru
Sobral
Fortaleza
Atol das Rocas
Fernando de Noronha
Aracati
Teresina
Areia Branca
Macau
Ponta do Calcanhar
Natal
Cabedelo
Campina
Grande
Recife
Pesqueira
Caruaru
Tamandaré
Maragogi
Juàzeiro
Maceió
Coruripe
Piaçabuçu
Aracaju

45°

30°

(Chart drawn by LCDR John Jones, USN)

a salute of 17 guns in honor of the birth of a female heir apparent to the Throne of Brazil.

[Ship's Clerk B.F. Stevens described conditions in Rio de Janeiro after the start of the Mexican War:

"Our second, or return visit to the beautiful city of Rio, was an exceedingly pleasant one, for Mr. Henry A. Wise and his family were living only a short distance from the busy haunts of the city. They received and entertained us right royally.

"But the war with Mexico had been declared and several battles on her soil had been fought, and the coffee vessels, to the number of sixteen, were detained in Rio awaiting naval protection from the United States when the Constitution hove in sight to be their convoy home. So we took provisions and water for a sixty days' trip, and in a few days, bidding our friends farewell, we started for Boston, the home of 'Old Ironsides'."]

August 5, 1846 -- At 3 p.m., the U.S. Sloop of War Saratoga came in and anchored near us. A boy named Domingo Borges was discharged.

At 6 a.m., the following morning, we unmoored and hove up the starboard anchor. At 7, we loosed sails and the topsails, crossed the topgallant and royal yards and set the sails. We got underway with boats from the squadron toward the mouth of the harbor. The squadron boats were used to tow out six American boats that we were to convoy home. Their names were: Barques Mazopha, Chenongo, and Margret Hugg, with Brigs Tweed, Fabin, and Abo. At 9, we casted off all boats except our own. At 10, we called our boats alongside. At 11:40, we let go the starboard anchor in 19 fathoms and veered to with 30 fathoms of chain.

August 6, 1846 -- At 2:30, hoisted in 1st. and 2nd. cutters. At 3:30, we made signals for the convoy to get underway. All hands were called to and hove up the anchor. We made sail and commenced beating out of the harbor ahead of the convoy. At 7 p.m., we burned a blue light. At 9, two guns were fired for the convoy to tack.

August 7, 1846 -- We had a scare just out to sea. At 3 p.m., three sails were discovered ahead. The convoy was ordered to close with a signal from one gun. At 4 p.m., five strange sail now in sight. By the mid watch, we spoke to the Brig Tweed, and by 8 p.m., all the convoy were in sight.

August 22, 1846 -- As we make our way toward Boston, the convoy has been growing in number. All are coffee boats and now number sixteen in all. We continue to signal by pennant or blue light and gun for tack as we have sighted again many strange sails.

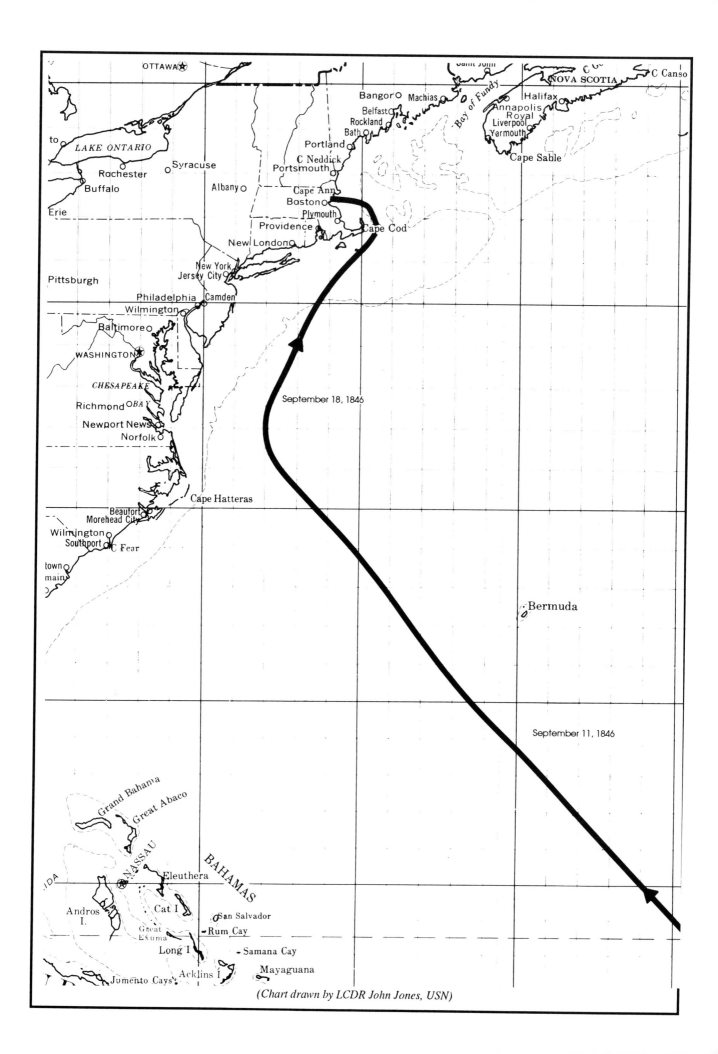

September 18, 1846

September 11, 1846

Bermuda

(Chart drawn by LCDR John Jones, USN)

At 7:30 a.m., 15 inches of water were reported to have leaked into the hold. We have had to continually reduce sail for the Barque Kareppa. Sick report 48 men. Latitude 4.09 north/Longitude 40.47 west.

August 25, 1846 -- At 4:30 p.m., the ship was pumped out. At 5:30, we went to quarters and the crew was inspected. At the approximate time, we signalled the convoy to begin closing. At 8 p.m., we discovered 6 inches in the hold. By 7:30, the hold had a total of 14 inches. The ship was pumped once again. At 9, the ship was tacked and the main sail was hauled up by 10 p.m. to allow the Margaret Hugg to come up with us. Latitude 8.06 north/Longitude 43.34 west.

September 11, 1846 -- While we were taking in all the studding sail to speak to the Schooner Joshua Brown from Provincetown, Thomas Hammons, gun mate, fell overboard. We picked him up by a line from the main chains. A boat was lowered for the life buoy.

Several of the men have been punished for gambling and asleep on the watch. Latitude 29.14 north/Longitude 66.29 west.

September 18, 1846 -- At 2 p.m., we discovered a brig under a jury mast [temporary rigging and mast -- a jury mast might consist of a large yard or any available spar] on the weather bow. At 3:40 p.m., we hove to and sent a boat to her. The boat returned at 4:30 with Lieutenant Hall, Commander of the U.S. Survey Brig Washington. He reported that on the 8th. of September, she was dismasted near the Capes of Virginia and that her Commander, Lieutenant [George M.] Bache, and 10 of the crew were washed overboard and drowned. [The brig Washington had been transferred to the Coast Survey in 1840 following conversion from a revenue cutter and was dismasted during a storm in Chesapeake Bay as the Thomas journal noted.]

We then got the gig and sparrow boat over the side and took the Washington in tow. We also sent onboard of her some light sails of our own. We also sent some articles over to her crew as well and then got underway. It should be noted that Lieutenant Bache was a descendant of Benjamin Franklin. Many of our convoy are beginning to break off and return to their home ports. [Without the help given as described by Thomas, it is probable that the Washington would have been lost. However, because of the Constitution's intervention, the brig returned to Gosport shipyard, Portsmouth, Virginia and was repaired.] Latitude 36.39 north/Longitude 73.00 west.

September 22, 1846 -- At 3 p.m., the water has begun to shoal as we haul up. Some of the officers boarded the American Brig Linden from Charleston bound for New York. At 5:30 p.m., we hoisted the jack to get a pilot as there are a number of sails around us.

At 6 p.m., we received a pilot. The pilot boat Enoch Tuhley took the Brig Washington in tow. She is to sail with the pilot ship inside the Capes of Delaware. Before she casted off, we received the Brig's coast pilot, B. F. Richardson. A New York pilot has also boarded.

September 26, 1846 -- During this day, we had variable winds and some thick fog at times. There are several sails now in sight. We have roused the starboard chain, overhauled it and payed [drawn or pulled] it below again.

The stream anchor has been placed on the bow and the stream cable has been bent [The process of attaching a cable to anchor by taking the rope's end through the anchor ring then turning it around the bight, making a clinch which is then seized. The seizings are referred to properly as the bends.]. At 3 a.m., the lanyard was parted and the martingale [rope or chain passing down from the jib-boom to the wood or metal spar, dolphin striker, pointing down from the end of the bowsprit] hauled down. Dan B. Perry, boy, was punished with one dozen lashes of the colt for missing his muster.

The ship was pumped out. We are having to sound frequently through this day from 46 to 18 fathoms. We have made and reduced sail as becomes necessary. We are now making the best of our way for the port of Boston.

[Thus ends the USS *Constitution's* voyage around the world.]

Epilogue

On Sunday, September 27, 1846, "Old Ironsides" arrived safely in Boston Harbor after having logged 55,000 miles and shown the flag to a number of foreign ports that had never seen an American warship. Finally on Monday, September 28, 1846, she was towed to Charlestown Navy Yard, her official "home port," where the crew was mustered and personally congratulated by Captain Percival for a job well done.

After several days of "squaring away" the ship, carpenter Henry George Thomas left Boston for Hampton Roads and Gosport. Stored within his sea chest among his other belongings was the journal you have read.

Ship's carpenter Henry George Thomas lived out his remaining days in Norfolk, Virginia where he was a familiar and welcome sight at the Gosport shipyard. There he trained apprentices to follow in the tradition of his trade. Because of a hernia sustained while on duty, he was officially retired from the Navy and died in 1876. However, it is a tribute to Henry George Thomas and the care he took for the USS *Constitution* that she remains in service to her country today.

USS *Constitution*
A Brief History

In 1794, when Constitution and five other frigates were authorized for construction, the newly formed government of the United States had been without a navy for nine years.

During this period, the nation became increasingly dependent upon international trade.   American merchants found it increasingly dangerous to trade with Mediterranean nations because of frequent attacks from the Barbary (North African) pirates.   Finally, on March 27, 1794, Congress passed a bill to establish the U.S. Navy.   Constitution, laid down that same year, was designed by Joshua Humphreys and Josiah Fox to be powerful enough to defeat any foe in the same class and fast enough to outsail a stronger opponent.

Built by Colonel George Claghorn at Edmond Harrt's shipyard in Boston, the live oak, red cedar, white oak, pitch pine and locust of which she was constructed came from states ranging from Maine to South Carolina and Georgia.   The live oak, which grows predominantly on our southeastern coast, came from the sea islands off Georgia. Her masts came from Unity, Maine, and South Carolina furnished the pine for her decks.   Some of the canvas came from Rhode Island, and New Jersey provided the keel and cannon balls.   Sails, gun carriages, and the anchors came from Massachusetts.   Boston silversmith Paul Revere provided the spikes and copper sheathing.

Constitution truly is in all respects a national ship. Today, only about ten per cent of the original ship exists. The rest has been restored over the years, but it is the live oak, forming the backbone of the ship, that has remained strong and made it possible to restore and rebuild her.

On October 21, 1797, USS *Constitution* slid down the ways, just three years from the laying of her keel.   The total cost was $302,718, as expensive to our young economy then as modern warships are to us today.

In 1798, French cruisers began to interfere with American commerce to such an extent that while the United States did not actually declare war on France, all treaties between the two governments were abrogated and American ships were commissioned to patrol the East Coast and West Indies in order to capture French vessels.   Under the command of Capt. Samuel Nicholson, Constitution served in the so-called "Quasi-War" with France.

In 1801, the nation once again turned its attention to the Barbary pirates after merchantmen were forced to pay more than a million dollars in tribute to the Dey of Algiers. The Bashaw of Tripoli added insult to injury by cutting down the flagstaff at the American consulate on May 10 of that year, thus declaring war on the United States.

USS *Constitution* was named as Commodore Edward Preble's flagship, and now with a fleet, the U.S. Navy sailed for the Mediterranean. Arriving there in 1803, Commodore Preble blockaded the port of Tripoli. When a peaceful settlement of affairs could not be reached, Constitution bombarded the fortifications and gunboats around the harbor. In 1804, Constitution returned to blockade duty under command of Commodore John Rodgers who forced the Tripolitan pirates to sign a treaty in his cabin by which they ceased their demands for tribute and agreed to release all American prisoners. Commodore Rodgers then sailed to Tunis where he dictated a similar treaty with the Bey aboard Constitution in 1805.

When the United States fought its second war with England in 1812, Constitution was commanded by Capt. Isaac Hull. After a desperate chase by a British squadron of five warships, Constitution was able to outrun the enemy in a calm over two days by using kedge anchors and being towed by longboats rowed by the crew. From Boston, the ship put to sea again, sailing along the coast of Nova Scotia. On August 19, Constitution met HMS *Guerriere*, which, once in range of the Americans, opened fire. Constitution then bore down on the enemy in silence. Impatiently the men stood at their quarters; the gunners awaited the order to fire. Not until the ships were abreast did Captain Hull give the word, "Now, boys, pour it into them!"

Constitution's entire broadside struck the Guerriere. In less than 20 minutes her mizzenmast went down. Constitution then passed ahead and sent a raking broadside tearing along the entire length of the enemy's decks, which cut away her rigging. It was during this engagement that a British sailor noted his shells simply bounced off the sides of the American ship, causing him to exclaim, "Her sides are made of iron!" In this 35-minute battle Constitution earned the title, "Old Ironsides." Guerriere struck her flag and the Constitution was on her way as a legend.

Less than five months later, Constitution, under Commodore William Bainbridge, secured her place in history by defeating HMS *Java* off Brazil. After being blockaded in Boston harbor, Constitution, with Capt. Charles Stewart at the helm, slipped past the British and sailed to Madeira in February 1815, where she defeated and captured HMS *Cyane* and *Levant*. When she reached New York on May 15 of that year, Constitution's reputation had eclipsed those of other national navies, including the British, as the world's most famous fighting ship.

However, after a cruise to the Mediterranean and a long layup, she was found to be unseaworthy and in 1830 was slated to be broken up. Had it not been for the poem by Oliver Wendell Holmes, Sr., titled "Old Ironsides," and the attention of thousands of Americans, the great ship surely would have been destroyed. Instead she became the first ship to enter the John Quincy Adams Drydock at Boston Navy Yard where she was extensively repaired and rebuilt.

From 1835 to 1855, Constitution made numerous voyages, the most important being her cruise around the world in 1844 under Capt. John "Madjack" Percival, during which she traveled 52,279 miles in 495 days at sea!

Following an inglorious career as a training vessel and receiving ship, Constitution was rebuilt in 1905 more as a relic than a warship. Finally, at Boston Navy Yard in 1925, a program was commenced to fully renovate Old Ironsides. Funds for the restoration were given in large part by the schoolchildren of America, who, like thousands of other Americans, had come to know the ship through the poem "Old Ironsides." She was again made "ship shape" for the nation's bicentennial, completing a turnaround cruise on June 17, 1976. On July 10, she got underway to lead the Tall Ships into Boston Harbor. The next day she made her third trip that year, to greet Queen Elizabeth II on board the Royal Yacht *Britannia*. Commencing in 1979, USS *Constitution's* annual turnaround date was fixed for the Fourth of July so this great warship could fire the national salute to celebrate our country's birthday!

Today, hundreds of thousands of Americans and tourists from around the world come to Boston to walk aboard America's most famous warship, still in commission, the United States Ship *Constitution*.

Constitution Statistics

Displacement: 2200 tons

Length Overall: 204 feet, billet head to taffrail
                 175 feet at waterline

Beam [width]: 43 feet, 6 inches

Draft: 22 feet, 6 inches

Foremast Height: 198 feet

Mainmast Height: 220 feet

Mizzenmast Height: 220 feet

Sail Area: 42,710 square feet

Speed: 13-plus knots

Armament: Thirty-two 24-pounder Long Guns; Range 1,200 yards
           Twenty 32 pounder Carronades; Range 400 yards
           Two 24-pounder Bow Chasers; Range 1,000 yards

Crew: 450, including 55 Marines and 30 Boys

Anchors: Two Main Bowers, 5,300 pounds each
          One Sheet Anchor, 5,400 pounds
          One Steam Anchor, 1,100 pounds
          Two Kedge Anchors, 700-400 pounds

Boats: One Longboat, 36 feet
           Two Cutters, 30 feet
           Two Whaleboats, 28 feet
           One Gig, 28 feet
           One Jolly Boat, 22 feet
           One Punt, 14 feet

Information for the Constitution's history and statistics graciously furnished by the United States Navy Historical Branch.

USS CONSTITUTION

AROUND-THE-WORLD CRUISE

APRIL 1844-SEPTEMBER 1846

JANUARY 1846

JUNE 1846

JULY 1846

MAY 1844

AUGUST 1846

OCTOBER 1844

NOVEMBER 1844

MAY 1845

OCTOBER 1845